MISS EMILY

Diane

Aunt Betty & Uncle Art
Christmas 1946

MISS EMILY

JEAN GOULD

illustrated by

URSULA KOERING

1946
BOSTON
HOUGHTON MIFFLIN COMPANY

The Riverside Press
CAMBRIDGE · MASSACHUSETTS · PRINTED IN THE U.S.A.

To Jessie Dowd Stafford,
who first introduced me to Emily

CONTENTS

MISS
EMILY

CHAPTER ONE

S HE HAD NOT ALWAYS been called Miss Emily. She was named
Emily Elizabeth Dickinson. Her father, with his sharp,
stern eyes and high forehead, his black broadcloth suit and
high black stock neatly tied, took down the big, gilt-edged family
Bible and wrote into it:

> 'Emily Elizabeth Dickinson; born near midnight,
> Dec. 11th, 1830; Amherst, Massachusetts.'

The yellow candlelight flickered on the page, and through the
window the moonlight gleamed on the white marble fireplace and
the highly polished mahogany furniture his wife, Emily Norcross,
had brought with her by oxcart over hill and dale when she married
Squire Dickinson. The doctor had left a good half an hour before.
Mrs. Dickinson and the baby Emily were sleeping quietly, and the
Squire had blown out the astral lamps and lit his bedtime candle,
ready to retire. Yet here he sat, staring at the fly-leaf of the great
Bible, telling himself that his was a deep responsibility, now he had
two children, the older a boy and then this little girl.

'She must be a good child,' he said to himself. 'She must be
gentle and mild, like her mother whose namesake she is. And she
must be obedient and willing and well-trained in mind and soul.'

He closed the book, placed it back on the library shelf, and took
up the candle. As if in retort to his words, a loud wail arose from

1

the bedroom, and the Squire hurried upstairs to quiet the baby lest she waken her mother.

Hannah was already by the cradle, her long flannel nightgown trailing the floor, her cap a white peak in the moonlight.

She rocked the cradle back and forth. 'Quiet, my little one, quiet.' But the wail only grew worse.

Mr. Dickinson became impatient. 'I'll do it, Hannah,' he said. 'I don't want Mrs. Dickinson disturbed.' He rocked the cradle more vigorously, but Emily only cried more loudly. 'Hush,' her father admonished his newly born daughter. 'Hush.' The baby kept on, however, until at last the man picked her up, blanket and all.

'Hush,' he whispered again in his deep, sonorous voice. His strong arms held the baby firmly. She quieted down finally, and the Squire put her in the cradle once more. She was such a tiny thing, this new Emily Dickinson. You could scarcely see any rise beneath the blankets, and only a tuft of auburn hair showed above the little face. She had fallen asleep again, and the Squire mused above her as he stood gazing. Hannah had slipped quietly back to her room.

'Red hair,' he said to himself. 'And a chin of strong determination. You have your mother's name, Emily, but whose disposition have you?' He knew the answer to that already. It was his own, and the thought made him uneasy. 'Whose will your mind resemble, Emily? Whose soul will yours be like?'

These questions the Squire was not able to answer, until the last years of his life, and even then Emily Dickinson often puzzled her father. He loved her deeply, but he never completely understood her.

❧

SQUIRE DICKINSON, born and bred to strict Puritan tradition, was a tall, solemn New England man, who took his tall, solemn hat and

2

his cane every morning and walked down Main Street to his office, thinking tall, solemn thoughts to himself. If he met townsmen he knew, he would lift his glossy beaver hat to them, nod silently, and walk on until he came to the crossing at Main and Pleasant Streets, where he would go into his law office. Here he would work hard until lunch time, when he walked back home. After lunch, he would return on foot to his office for the afternoon, and then back home in the evening. He never varied this routine and never drove his horses except on special occasions. Every day, no matter how cold or hot the weather, the town of Amherst saw its leading citizen pass by with his inevitable top hat and cane.

It was the top hat and cane that caused the trouble one rainy morning. Emily, who in a few years had become a spirited, fun-loving little girl, knew her father might come downstairs at any moment, and that he would frown with disapproval if he caught her, but the temptation to mimic him was so strong within her that she couldn't resist.

'Look!' she said to the others, pointing to the vestibule. 'There's Father's tall' — here she stretched her face out in a long grimace — 'silk topper and cane. I'm going to try them on.'

Austin, her older brother, and Lavinia, three years younger than Emily, giggled with delight at their sister, whose recklessness was always a source of wonder and admiration.

'You wouldn't dare!' challenged Austin, his brown eyes shining with excitement at the prospect.

'Oh, wouldn't I?' retorted Emily, with a shake of her unruly curls. 'Here!' She seized the hat and popped it on the back of her head. In contrast to her dark red hair, it looked exactly like a stovepipe, sunk low over her ears. Her nose stuck out like a straight little stick, her mouth was small and determined and her chin was strong. Emily's eyes, now peeping out from beneath the hat so laughing and full of fun, were nearly the color of her hair. They had the glint of russet sunsets and, more often than not, their expression was unfathomable. At the moment they were pure mischief, and she was a grotesque little figure as she paraded up and down the front hall, holding the cane high and stiff like her father, and trying to keep his hat from slipping down as she imitated his sober walk.

'I'm Father,' she announced impressively. 'I'm going to the office.' As she passed Austin, she lifted the hat just as the Squire always did and nodded silently, moving past him with the same deliberate tread.

Austin and Lavinia squealed with enjoyment. 'It's true!' cried Austin. 'That's exactly the way he looks!'

'Now walk by me,' begged Lavinia, clapping her hands.

Emily turned her steps in front of Vinnie and was in the act of raising the hat once more, when a deep voice thundered from the landing. 'Well, Emily? What is the meaning of this performance?'

Austin and Lavinia scampered out to the back hall, leaving Emily to face her father alone. He came down the remaining steps like a judge. Without speaking, he took his hat from her head, drew the walking-stick from her hand, placed them on the stand near the door, and returned to the little girl.

'What excuse have you for touching my personal belongings?' he demanded.

Emily faced him unafraid, still half-amused at her own prank. 'I just wanted to give them a little practice, Father,' she said demurely, but behind her words there was rippling laughter about to break loose. The Squire could feel it, and this quality in his elder daughter worried the Squire more than anything else. Teasing laughter and gaiety were beyond his imagination.

'You know you are not supposed to touch my things,' he said rebukingly.

'I know. I'm sorry, Father.'

'Then why did you do it?'

'Well, I just wanted to have a little fun . . .'

'Fun! You were mocking me, mocking your father, Emily!' he accused her. 'That's a serious charge against you.'

4

'Not mocking, Father!' protested Emily. 'You know it's funny the way you walk downtown like Judgment Day . . .'

'Emily!' The Squire was always shocked by her figures of speech. 'You are being very impudent! Now go to your room for an hour.'

'But, Father, I didn't mean to be.' It was hard for Emily to see why her father became so irate over her simplest remarks.

'Silence!' he warned. 'Now go!' He pointed to the stairs.

Emily turned without another word and went up to her room. She was in a fury at her father because he would not let himself smile at these little jokes of hers. Surely he must know she loved him far too much to poke fun at him unkindly! She felt certain he could understand if he wanted to, and this made her angry. But she knew too well the rules of Puritan respect for one's parents to argue with him or to protest against his edict.

She never felt it was really a punishment to stay in her room, anyhow. Emily enjoyed being alone, for she could pretend and dream all she wanted, and there was no one to disapprove or tell her to stop. She drew a low rocker up to the window and sat gazing out through the rain as she rocked. Just outside was a whispering pine tree that swayed back and forth and sang its secrets to her when the night was darkest. What a strange, sad song it had, like someone sighing in the wind. What did it say? What was it sighing for?

She pulled her chair closer to the window, and climbed on her knees, leaning her elbows on the sill. The leaves were just beginning to uncurl, like pale green feathers blown out on the air. Although a wet spring mist hung like a veil above it, Emily could see the long slopes of the Holyoke mountain range which glowed purple in the distance. She imagined herself floating on a carpet of air, out over the treetops toward the range.

First she would circle the house — the Mansion, it was called by the people of Amherst, for it was by far the most stately residence in the village, with its white portico, its marble mantelpieces, and mar-

5

ble-topped tables. Then she would ride over the Dickinson grounds, past the flower garden, past the vegetable patch, and up over the barn. Maybe she would light on the roof for a moment and peek through one of the cracks that let in stray beams of sunlight when you went to gather the eggs so carefully hidden in each nest. The barn was one of Emily's favorite 'places,' for it was always full of dark excitement. She never knew what might be lurking in the shadows. Then she would glide away over the orchard, where pears and peaches, cherries and apples vied with each other in shining fullness when harvest-time came.

If it had been fall instead of spring, she would reach down and pluck a handful of nuts as she sped by the hickory, chestnut, and black-walnut trees that grew on the Dickinson grounds. Once more in front of the Mansion, looking down at the white picket fence which guarded the house all around before the hedge, Emily would hover over the dusty road to Boston town, waiting for the yellow stagecoach, drawn by four horses, to come pounding down the sanded ruts. It would be bringing passengers from faraway cities to stay at Elijah Boltwood's tavern at Main and Pleasant Streets, right near the town common.

Maybe she would race it into town. How startled the travelers would be to see a little girl riding on thin air outside the coach windows! Emily laughed aloud to think of it. Oh, she would beat them, she would beat them by a mile down to the common. Here she would sail across the heads of the townsfolk gathered for exchange of gossip, standing around in little groups upon arrival or departure. How horrified they would be! They would scatter toward the one-rail fence where their horses and buggies were hitched and their farm wagons tied, with cries of 'Witch! Witch!' just like their Puritan ancestors.

Then Emily would swoop down across the frog pond at one end of the common and the enclosure near the other end, where the stray animals were penned until someone claimed them; she would open the gate and let the dogs or cats or lost cows or whatever hap-

6

pened to be in there go free. They always looked so sad and frightened.

Before anyone could catch her, she would be out on her way toward Pelham Ridge or the Holyoke mountains!

At this point in her airy journey, the door opened softly behind her and Mrs. Dickinson stood framed in the doorway. Her hair was neatly parted above her calm face, her full calico dress, protected by a small black satin apron at the waist, fell stiffly to the floor, billowing way out at both sides; and beneath it, her little feet were two black-slippered points.

'Emily, my dear,' she said softly.

But Emily was still trailing the clouds on her imaginary carpet. Her head was between the starched white curtains and she neither saw nor heard her mother.

'Emily!' Mrs. Dickinson called a little more firmly.

There was a flash of copper against the curtain, and Emily turned around, sliding off her knees and out of the cane-seated rocker. 'Hello, Mother!' she smiled amiably. 'Ooh, my knees.' She began rubbing them, for the cane had left a pattern of indentations even through her ruffled pantaloons.

'Emily, my dear,' Mrs. Dickinson continued apologetically, 'I — I lost track of the time. You have been here an hour and a half, and your father said I should call you in an hour.'

Emily laughed. She never paid much attention to hours; she couldn't tell time anyhow. 'Never mind, Mother, it's all right. I wasn't here, anyway.'

'You weren't here? But where were you?' Mrs. Dickinson asked fearfully. Had the little girl disobeyed again, she wondered. Why couldn't Emily be like the others? She never had to worry about them.

'I was outdoors, flying over the house and down to the common. I beat the stage there, too!'

'Emily, Emily, how you do run on!' Mrs. Dickinson was relieved to learn it was only another one of Emily's odd dreams that would possess her by day as well as night. Yet the timid, gentle woman was distressed a little, because the child made it seem so real, as if she actually had been out there floating through the air. 'Emily Dickinson, how you do run on!' she repeated.

'I was on the way to Holyoke when you called,' Emily continued. 'Oh, you should have come along, Mother!'

'Never mind that,' Mrs. Dickinson said hastily, lest her daughter run on indefinitely. 'You may leave your room now. Here, let me smooth your pinafore.'

Emily tried to stand patiently while her mother straightened the pinafore and retied her sash. Her dreams were forgotten and she wondered what Austin and Vinnie were doing and where they were. 'Thank you, Mother.' But before her mother was quite finished, she ran off to find the others.

CHAPTER TWO

Austin! Vinnie! Austin! Where are you?' she called. For a moment there was no answer, and then, so low it could scarcely be heard, a slight giggle came drifting into the hall from somewhere close by. Emily's sensitive ears picked up the sound at once, though it had been quickly smothered.

The upper hall was as wide as a room, and at the wall opposite the stairs stood a chest with a ruffle around its high old-fashioned legs. Emily was sure the folds of the chintz moved ever so slightly, but she pretended not to notice. 'Austin, Vinnie!' she went on calling. She peeked in every bedroom and under every piece of furniture, but found neither her brother nor her sister.

'They must be in the cellar!' she said, quite loudly. Again came the suppressed giggle. Emily stamped her feet to imitate the sound of someone running downstairs, and in a moment out from beneath the ruffle of the highboy popped the two heads of Austin and Vinnie full of glee and triumph.

'We fooled her!' sang Vinnie.

But the victory was short-lived, for there stood Emily smiling wickedly at them. 'Who fooled whom?' she demanded.

'Nobody, I guess.' Austin was disgusted and a little bored. Ordinarily he would not have bothered playing with Vinnie when Emily was not around, but none of the children were allowed to play outdoors when it was rainy, nor even in the barn nor on the scullery floor as they sometimes did, so there was nothing left. He sighed. 'Vinnie always gives it away with her giggling, anyhow. What shall we do now?' He turned his quiet eyes questioningly toward his sisters.

'I don't know,' said Vinnie, with a pout on her pretty little face, shaking her dark head at him. 'What shall we do, Emily?'

Emily's sherry-colored eyes looked thoughtful for a moment. Then she jumped up, twinkling, and full of action. Her daydreams had given her an idea. 'I'm the stagecoach horses and I'm running away. You're the driver, Austin, and Lavinia's the people. Catch me, try to catch me!' And she started running around the hall, quickly and light as a deer.

Exciting, wonderful Emily! There was never a time when she failed to come forth with some good way to amuse them all. Whenever they were at a loss for something to do, it was always Emily who devised a new pastime. Now Austin ran after her, and Vinnie trailed along behind both of them. 'Not so fast,' she pleaded. It was a treat to have both Emily and Austin playing with her at the same time, and she wanted to keep up with them. She hurried her short little legs and managed to stay just behind Austin.

The game grew wild and noisy. Emily, full of impish tricks, stopped short once when Austin was nearly upon her, and then zigzagged off in the opposite direction, leaving her brother bewildered and far behind.

'No fair!' he panted, stopping to rest against the newel post.

Emily laughed delightedly. 'Why not?' she countered. 'Come on. You'll never catch a runaway horse that way!' Her pantalooned legs flew with renewed vigor as Austin came on in pursuit.

The children were not supposed to run in the house, and the harsh noise of their swift feet brought Mother and Hannah, who could not imagine what was causing such a racket upstairs, hurrying out of the kitchen.

'Children, children! What are you doing up there?' called their mother. But she had such a gentle voice they couldn't hear

10

it way up there, with three pairs of feet clattering on the waxed floor and three voices shouting with laughter. The children kept right on with their game.

Emily could run faster than Austin, but he was beginning to get closer and she was afraid he might catch her. She was feeling a little dizzy from running round and round in the hall, so when she came to the stairs, she went bounding down, with Austin right after her, just as her mother started to come up. Emily flew past her out to the back hall, but Austin stumbled on the stairs in his excitement and fell down halfway, bumping straight into Mrs. Dickinson.

'Children, children, this will have to stop,' she said. 'Austin, did you hurt yourself?'

Austin's knee was skinned a little.

'I must put something on it,' said his mother. 'And look! Your father is coming!'

At that all three children quieted down at once, and became most sober and solemn. Father! thought Emily with panic.

'Austin, come with me,' said Mother. 'Lavinia, you go to meet Father. And Emily, see that his paper is where it should be. Austin, he mustn't see you.' With this, his mother hurried Austin upstairs to put some ointment on his knee, straighten his clothes, and comb his hair. Vinnie went to the side door to let Father in the house and to take his high hat and gold-headed cane. Emily went into the parlor to see that his daily paper was on the little marble-topped table near the fireplace. She wondered how he would act toward her now.

Everything was calm and quiet by the time Squire Dickinson came to the door of the Mansion.

'Good evening, Father,' said Lavinia, and she held out her hands.

'Good evening, Daughter,' answered Mr. Dickinson, and he gave her his hat and cane. She went to put them in the vestibule, and Father went into the parlor.

11

'Good evening, Father,' said Emily, wondering if he would speak to her.

'Good evening, Emily.' Father rested his hand for just a second on Emily's auburn head. 'Have you spent a useful day?'

'I think so,' said Emily.

Father sat down in his chair by the fireplace, and picked up his paper. 'Have you learned anything new today?' he asked his daughter. He did not mention their clash; it was over, finished.

'No, Father, not today,' answered Emily. 'It was too rainy for new things. They're waiting for sunshine,' she added, smiling.

Father sat for a few minutes without saying a word. Emily stood watching him, not daring to leave until he dismissed her. She would have liked to go up closer to him and maybe lean on his shoulder while he read the paper, but Father never seemed to let anyone come close to him. He was far away, and so Important. He was someone stern and wonderful.

'Come here, Emily,' he said at last.

Emily walked up and stood within a foot of Father's chair.

He took his big gold watch from his waistcoat pocket. 'I think you are old enough to learn to tell time,' he said. He pressed a spring, and the cover of the watch flew back.

Emily laughed. 'A jack-in-the-box ought to pop out,' she said.

Her father did not notice that she had spoken.

'Listen carefully to everything I have to say,' he said solemnly. 'You know I never repeat my words.'

'Yes, Father,' said Emily.

'Now,' said Father, sounding like a teacher, 'let us begin. There are twenty-four hours in every day. Hours are divided into minutes, and minutes into seconds. The short hand points to the hours, and the long hand to the minutes. There are two sets of hours, as one o'clock in the morning and one o'clock in the afternoon. When the long hand is at three, it is fifteen minutes after the hour, or a quarter past.'

12

Emily wanted to ask 'why?' but she knew she must not ask any questions. It would interrupt Father.

He went on and on explaining. Emily listened to him closely, for no one had ever taught her anything about the way to tell time. Now she was getting it all at once, and it seemed very complicated and confusing, but she didn't let Father know. She just nodded her head, and said 'Yes, Father,' and looked as if she understood till he was through.

When he had finished, he snapped the heavy gold lid closed and put his watch back in his waistcoat pocket. He nodded his head to her and picked up his paper. Emily could not ask him to tell her again, though there were many points of which she wasn't sure. She looked at him hesitatingly, but he was already reading, lost in the paper. She tiptoed softly from the room.

In the hall stood the big old grandfather's clock. Emily stopped in front of it and looked at its old yellow face, with the little hand pointing to six and the big hand pointing to nine.

She hadn't the faintest idea what time it was.

IN A FEW DAYS the weather cleared, and the sun shone warm and smiling on the Mansion grounds. Its rays pried open the tiny white fists of the syringa buds. Spreading, they sent their soft spring fragrance in through the doors and windows and brought Emily out on mercurial feet. She sniffed the small white blossoms and held her face up to the sky, letting the breeze play among her bronze curls. What a beautiful day! She took a few skips on the walk, then stopped suddenly to listen to a robin trilling in a near-by tree.

'I know!' she exclaimed all at once.

She went running into the house to find Mother. In her hurry she let the door slam behind her as she ran through the center hall calling, 'Mother! Mother!'

'And pray, what is this hurly-burly about?' asked a deep voice.

It was Father, just taking his hat and cane to leave for the office.

'Oh, Father!' Emily stopped in her tracks. She was well aware of her father's attitude toward slammed doors, running feet, and loud voices. 'It wasn't me, it was my Grandmother Gunn!' she explained with twinkling eyes, referring to the grandmother whose antics livened the family history.

Her father ignored this story, used by all the children to explain away their misdemeanors.

'Emily,' he said gravely, 'doors are to be closed, not slammed. In addressing people, we use the speaking tone, not hog-calling. And if we respect our home, we walk sedately through its halls, not run like hoodlums.'

'I'm sorry, Father.' Emily did so hate to displease her father.

Having delivered his sermon, her father looked down at his little daughter not unkindly. 'Now, what is this hurly-burly about?' he repeated, the ghost of a smile appearing in his eyes.

'Oh, Father, I just had an idea. I thought how nice it would be if Helen Fisk could come over to play under the syringas today!'

'I believe it could be arranged,' said her father. 'Your mother can dispatch a note with Tom. I presume you will find her in the kitchen.'

'Oh, thank you, Father!' Emily, all happiness once more, started with nimble feet on a run toward the back hall, but remembering almost immediately, she slowed down and walked quietly in the direction of the kitchen door.

Mother was busy straining currants for jelly, but as soon as she finished, she wrote a note to Professor Fisk's wife, asking if Helen might play with Emily and Lavinia under the syringas in the afternoon. Tom went off with the little blue envelope, and Emily and Vinnie hung at the front gate waiting for his return.

He was soon back, with a reply for Mrs. Dickinson. It read: 'Professor Fisk will lead Helen over to play with Emily beneath the

14

syringas, this afternoon. In case it prove not convenient to send her home, he will call for her in the chaise toward nightfall, before the dew falls.'

Emily jumped up and down, and Vinnie clapped her hands. They both loved to play with Helen Fisk, who could think up all sorts of delightful variations on 'playing house,' favored pastime of all the little girls in Amherst.

Promptly at three o'clock, Helen arrived with her father. She was merry as an elf, with curls that bobbed around her laughing face, dancing eyes, and a turned-up nose.

Lavinia was not quite sure she was included in the plans. 'Can I play, too?' she inquired timidly.

'Of course, Vinnie,' Emily assured her; and Helen, with sudden inspiration, suggested, 'You're the father, and you have to go to the office every day.'

So everyone was satisfied, and the three settled down to their game. In the flowering bush above their heads the bees hummed as they worked among the yellow stamens. 'They're keeping house, too,' said Emily.

All afternoon the three played under the syringa, while Mother watched them from the window as she sewed. When the sun set behind Pelham Ridge, Professor Fisk appeared at the front gate to call for Helen. Good-byes were said, and promises to come again soon. At the last minute Emily remembered a picture she had cut from a Boston catalogue to show Helen.

'I won't be a moment!' she called over her shoulder. She went running into the house, and the door slammed shut behind her!

Edward Dickinson came down the road at that moment, and he stopped before the gate to chat with Professor Fisk. His fine, dark eyebrows raised at the sound of the slammed door, and after Emily had returned to show her picture and the others had gone, he said: 'Emily, I think you and I had better take a little walk.'

'Yes, Father,' said Emily. She took hold of his hand, and they went through the white gate together into the dusty road.

15

'Emily,' the Squire began in his solemn tones, 'it is time you learned to control yourself, to act in a manner befitting our honored ancestors.' As they walked along the quiet country road, Emily's father retold the story of the Dickinson family, from Nathaniel, who landed in Massachusetts in 1630, to Samuel Fowler Dickinson, Emily's grandfather, who had founded Amherst Academy and Amherst College. He reminded her that these men had walked with God all their lives. They fought for their right to worship; they battled the Indians; they struggled for freedom from England; they tried to spread education, for learning was almost a passion with them; and they never for a moment forgot their Creator, living in righteous fear of His judgment.

Emily heard the grave, steady voice of her father, but she did not listen as closely as she might have. She had heard the story before, and it was such a beautiful day. There was so much to see. She looked about for buttercups in the meadow or perhaps some early violets. The sun was setting in the soft spring sky, and Emily felt quite sure she could only love the God who had made such a sky. How could you fear Him?

But Father talked on about the Judgment Day and about leading a life that was faultlessly pure. 'You must remember your heritage, Emily,' he said. 'You must learn to conduct yourself quietly and to walk in the fear of the Lord at all times.'

Emily caught his last sentence as she was trying to see if that was really a bluebird in the elm tree ahead. She sighed a little, for her conscience bothered her. 'I'll try, Father,' she promised.

CHAPTER THREE

S HE DID TRY. Emily wanted to please her father. She wanted to be a true New England daughter, but it was hard, especially on Sunday. As Emily grew older, she found it harder and harder to face the Sabbath every week, held in the strictest observance by the people of Amherst. It was such a long, dull sober day, like a face without any expression.

Every Sunday morning, Squire Dickinson and his family went to church. Father and Mother walked ahead, Father in his best black broadcloth suit and black stock, and Mother in her best black silk, her arm just resting on his. Austin, Emily, and Vinnie walked behind their parents.

'I wish we were on the way to school,' Emily breathed to Austin one Sunday, for school was exciting now that she was twelve years old. She and Vinnie had started going to Amherst Academy this term, and Emily felt as though she were just waking up; there was so much to learn and so much to think about. How different the Academy was from the little public school with its baby lessons learned by memory while sitting on bare wooden benches!

Austin nodded, giving her a quick smile without speaking that told his agreement. Father preferred no conversation on the way to church. Emily understood his silence and contented herself with the knowledge that Austin felt the way she did. She was quite sure no one else had a brother like Austin. How handsome he looked in his black suit with its wide white collar!

She and Vinnie were dressed in their Sunday best, too, fussy dresses with puffed sleeves and frilly round lace collars. Too fussy, Emily thought, to go with the short, closely cropped haircuts, almost like boys', she and Vinnie had now. She took a skip to get in time with the other two and for a while watched their feet marching along like soldiers. They were all wearing high buttoned shoes, made of the finest leather Father could find. He was very particular about such things. But after she had kept in step, going along quietly and carefully like the others for a good part of the way, Emily began to give a little hop or jump every now and then, or turn her head completely around to see a robin she had just heard.

Spring was coming around the next corner; you could feel it in every breath of air. The buds looked bulgy. The sky was a pale wash of blue. Emily thought it would be pleasant to have church out-of-doors, where you could look right up to heaven all the time.

All too soon they reached the church. It was a large, square building made of yellow brick, with four enormous white columns on the front of the porch. Inside, the big windows were without curtains, and the only heat was from the stoves in the vestibule, which had pipes leading down the outside aisles of the church and sent precious little heat to those who sat in the center. It was always too hot or too cold, and to sit for long hours in discomfort while the minister thundered away about the Devil and destruction seemed a difficult task to Emily. She sighed a little as they made their way down to the Dickinson pew. But tomorrow was Monday, and there would be a whole new week stretching out in front of her.

Father opened the little door at the end of the pew and held it for everyone to enter. Emily signaled to him to wait a minute before 'buttoning them in tight' as she called it. She had brought a narcissus from her indoor garden for old Mrs. McGuiness, whose aged legs were stiff with rheumatism. Walking down the aisle to the elderly lady's pew, Emily slipped the flower on the seat for a

18

surprise. Then she returned to the Dickinson pew, and Father snapped the door closed.

A moment later, the minister came in and took his place behind the pulpit. This was so narrow the preacher showed in patches from in back of it, and unless he was careful with his elbows when he made a gesture, he would bang into its sides. Emily cast a look at Vinnie and Austin when the minister began to get excited, and the three of them slid forward in the pew to see if he would forget and fling out his arm. He was already shouting and pounding his right fist into the palm of his left hand. If he should happen to throw out his right as he brought it back . . . Would he whack himself this morning, or would he remember to draw in at the last moment? Three pairs of Dickinson eyes stared tensely, glued to the minister. He was very careful! It was something of a disappointment, and they all leaned back with a sigh and relaxed.

After a sermon lasting for several hours, church was over for the morning, and the Dickinson family walked home and sat down to the good dinner which had been cooked for them. Father sat at the head of the table and gave the blessing. A fire was glowing in the Franklin stove which stood at one end of the room, and the silver on the sideboard gleamed in the lights from the blaze. Emily felt like eating today. The cold which had kept her out of school for most of the week was gone, and it would not be long till the spring flowers came and the apple blossoms would be blowing about the orchard. She ate a full dinner and Father looked pleased. When she wasn't well, or hadn't much appetite, he worried about her.

As soon as they had finished, Father rose and led them all to the library, where he took down the great Bible. 'Today I am going to read to you from the Book of Job,' he said. He read for an hour. His strong, clear voice, his manner of reading, made you listen. Emily, seated on a small hassock, leaned her chin on her hands and looked up into his calm face as he pronounced the words. How sure Father was in everything he did! She wondered if she would ever feel certain that her every action was so right. Maybe when that happened you were grown up.

When he came to the end of the chapter, Father closed the book and put it back on the shelf. 'Now we will all rest,' he issued his usual Sunday afternoon order.

The family went upstairs to observe the customary period of quiet, each retiring to his own room. Emily tried to take a nap, but she couldn't sleep, and kept hopping up to the window, looking out at the trees and the birds and the sky. Now that she was twelve, she was full of the wish to be doing something every minute. Still, it was the time for rest and she decided to try to sleep.

She lay down on the big fourposter bed again, but no sleep would come. There was something moving in the pine branches. What could it be? She was at the window in a moment, peering out into the tree, nose pressed against the pane. The branches stirred with a quick, darting movement, but it was hard to see what caused it. Then, as she watched, Emily saw a slender, shy, brown bird emerge for a moment, only to disappear again.

It was the thrush; he had come back early! And he had remembered that she had been in the habit of sprinkling crumbs on the sill for him. He must be hungry now, it was still wintry out.

She opened her door and stole into the hall without a sound. Moving noiselessly toward the stair, for no one could go more quietly than Emily when she chose, she sped down the back way with soundless steps, and slipped into the kitchen. She hurried across the wide kitchen floor to the cabinet where the bread loaves were lined up, under a snowy napkin. Neat Hannah would not tolerate a single crumb anywhere, so Emily had to cut off a bit and break it up in her fingers, still softly, quickly, before she was discovered.

Then she crept back upstairs to her room and closed the door again. She opened the window a tiny crack and pushed the crumbs onto the sill. The thrush was waiting, for there was a flick of evergreen needles almost immediately and out he hopped, eyeing her

questioningly, head on one side. With hesitating, short flights, he came closer and closer, till at last he was on the ledge, pecking gratefully at the bread crumbs.

Emily watched him with delight and satisfaction. Who else could have reached the kitchen during rest period on Sunday, when you weren't supposed to leave your room, have found the food, and come back without disturbing a soul? She laughed to herself and waved at the thrush, who was far too busy to notice. In a few minutes he had devoured every bit and flown back to the refuge of the tree.

Then suddenly there came a rush of sweet high notes, the song of the thrush. He was thanking her! Emily flung wide the window to listen. For some moments the melody continued as she stood transfixed. Then, just as suddenly, the song was ended and the thrush had flown away.

Emily closed the window, but stood there looking out for several minutes after the bird had disappeared. What a beautiful song! And it had been sung to her, she was sure. She was singing inside as she turned away.

She moved unconsciously to her little mahogany desk. She felt like writing, telling somebody about the thrush's song. She owed Jane Humphrey a letter. But when the date was on the paper — 'March 25, 1842' — and the words, 'My dear Jane,' Emily sat nibbling her pen and dreaming thoughts that tinkled like a melody.

She wrote down lines, two, three, four of them, rapidly. They seemed to come out of nowhere, and she stared down at them in surprise. Had she really written those words? Miss Adams said Emily was an exceptional student in English. Perhaps she could be more than that — perhaps she could be . . .

She got up and went whirling around the room, her dress a ruffled balloon around her legs. How wonderful to know she might have a gift; she might one day be famous if she worked hard enough. It was so exciting! But she wouldn't tell a soul; she would keep it a secret until she was sure. She laughed to think what Father would say.

Then, remembering it was Sunday and she had been up all during the rest, she forced herself to lie down again for the few remaining minutes. But her eyes were open and her body tense.

Five minutes later, promptly at four o'clock, the church bells began to peal out softly. It was time for afternoon service. Emily jumped up and folded the paper on her desk hastily, shoving it into the farthest corner of the first pigeonhole. She brushed her hair with quick, hard strokes, smoothed her dress, and went to join the others in the downstairs hall. Her eyes were still shining.

They were already there, Austin and Vinnie, Father and Mother, forming a little square group. As she reached the last step, Father opened the front door and they all set out.

After they had started and the children had dropped behind, Austin shot Emily a questioning look. He had noticed her expression, she knew, and was curious to find out what caused it; but she turned away, pretending to be interested in something across the road.

'Come on, Emily, what is it?' he could not resist asking under his breath.

She stared at him in mock surprise, a smile hovering around her lips.

'You've got something up your sleeve,' he continued. 'What is it?'

But she shook her head, still smiling. 'Sh-h,' she warned, adding, 'I can't tell you now. Maybe sometime.' She didn't want anybody, not even Austin, to know her secret.

He shrugged and gave it up, while Vinnie regarded them both with the utmost curiosity. They were always so mysterious, those two, she thought as the three of them went along.

Afternoon service was not as long, nor as dull as the morning one. There were devotions, the choir sang squeakily, and the minister gave a short sermon, followed by the closing prayer.

Outside the congregation stood around in little groups speaking in hushed, gentle tones befitting the day.

'There's Helen Fisk,' said Austin to Emily. 'And I see Ned Clark.' He left the girls and made his way over to where a boy of about his age stood leaning against the pillar.

Emily was glad to see Helen as it had been more than a week since the girls had last been together. 'Hello, Helen!' she called.

'Hello, Emily! Are you coming back to school tomorrow? You miss the fun when you have to stay home — and we miss you!' Helen's merry eyes danced. Whenever there was no entertainment, she would make her own somehow, even on a staid, quiet Sunday.

'Yes, I'm coming,' Emily nodded. 'My cold's let me out of its cage. How much did I miss? What are they taking up?'

'We've had two more declensions in Latin,' Helen counted off on her fingers. 'And Miss Adams has assigned three compositions for next week.'

'Pooh, I've already written three extra,' said Emily. She laughed. 'I write more compositions than Miss Adams can read!'

'But Miss Adams doesn't mind, I know. Yours are the best in class, Emily.' Helen looked at her fondly, with an admiration she was always to feel for her auburn-haired friend.

Emily's cheeks grew warm with pleasure, but she said loyally, 'Not any better than yours or Emily Fowler's!'

Helen waved her away. 'You're being polite and you know it.'

'Well, anyhow,' — Emily's eyes were suddenly twinkling — 'no one can write compositions like Willy Lester!'

Both girls burst into laughter, for no papers in English class were duller than Willy's. It was boring from start to finish when he began to read.

'Come, Emily.' It was the Squire, who now approached them. 'We are waiting.'

'Yes, Father,' said Emily. She bade Helen good-bye and went with him to join the rest of the family.

At home they had tea, which Mother poured from a beautiful silver teapot. They ate little sandwiches and some caraway cookies and pudding. The Sunday night meal was always a simple one.

Then they went into the library again, and Father read evening family services. When he was through, he took out his gold watch. 'It's bedtime,' he said.

Mother went up to help the girls lay out their clothes for the next day. Emily was full of thoughts of school, but when she started to undress, she remembered the paper in her desk and went to hide it in a drawer of the bureau before Mother came from Vinnie's room. Sundays might not seem so dull any more; she could work during rest period. At other times, all through the week, there were school lessons to be done or Vinnie was around, but now she had found a time of solitude for the expression of all the thoughts she felt way down inside!

'Now, Emily, my dear,' her mother was saying as she came in the door, 'what about the blue challis for you tomorrow?'

She fussed and fluttered about quietly till it was all settled exactly what Emily was to put on. Then there was the question of clean socks for Austin, and she hurried off down the hall.

At last her duties were dispatched, and she saw that her three children were getting ready to retire with as little noise as possible in order not to disturb Father, who was reading. She went down to join him for a while.

As soon as she was gone, Emily took out the paper and read it over. Maybe it wasn't any good, maybe it was very bad; but it was a beginning — and her very own. She stood hugging the little paper against her nightdress for some time before she climbed into bed.

Downstairs the Squire and Mrs. Dickinson sat in their chairs before the fireplace; but soon he was nodding over his book, and Mother stifled a yawn over her embroidery. A little later, Father blew out the oil lamps and they went to bed, too.

Outside, the night held a starry softness, and a deep stillness. Everybody was asleep. Sunday in Amherst, 1842, was over, and Emily Dickinson had made a discovery.

26

CHAPTER FOUR

S HE AWOKE early the next morning, as if the memory of the
day before had tapped her on the shoulder. What fun to
have a secret — like stumbling on a hidden treasure box and
not telling anyone about the find. She clasped her shoulders and
laughed softly to herself.

She felt like getting up, though the rest of the household was
still asleep and the only stirring was the sound of Hannah beginning
to move around in the kitchen. Perhaps if Emily got to school
ahead of time, she would be able to catch a glimpse of Miss Adams
by herself, before the rest of the students arrived. It was wonderful
to talk to Miss Adams, for she always understood and encouraged
questions and ideas, and never raised her eyebrows in disapproval,
or put her pupils off as if they were impudent children. She listened
carefully to what they had to say, weighing each opinion as if it
had come from an adult.

It had been hard to miss her class for a whole week, and Emily
was anxious to see her favorite teacher again. She threw back the
covers, shivering as her feet touched the cold floor. The fire in the
little stove had gone out, and the room felt chilly and damp. But
no matter, she would get dressed, anyhow.

Hannah, who had forgotten her shawl, came upstairs as Emily
was halfway though. 'Im-ly,' she scolded, 'what're ye gettin'

27

dressed for, with the room cold as ice, an' no fire laid yet in the stove? Have ye no sense, girl?'

Emily laughed at her. 'I just felt like getting up early, Hannah,' she explained; 'I want to be at school before the rest.'

'I see.' Hannah stood with her fists dug into ample hips, her short, powerful body enveloped in a huge mother-hubbard apron. Her eyes snapped. 'And I suppose ye want to be down again with the cold, too, and I havin' to doctor ye! Now, back to bed till I lay a fire.' And she whisked Emily back under the covers, half-clad, while she tramped downstairs for wood and a small bucket of coal.

Emily plumped up her pillow and leaned back on it, crossing her arms behind her head. As well wrestle with the Devil as try to stand up against Hannah when her mind was set on something. None of the family was supposed to rise till the little stoves had taken off the chill — and that was that. Emily resigned herself to waiting, and soon Hannah returned, bearing an armful of wood and the coal.

The fire was going at last, and since the weather was not really cold, it didn't take long for the room to become comfortable — or at least for Emily, in her impatience, to decide it was warm enough to dress. She hurried into the rest of her clothes, washed herself in icy water rather than wait for a pitcher of hot from the kitchen, and was ready to go downstairs as the others rose from their beds.

She did not save much time, because Father must have all his family together at mealtimes, and no one could eat until they were all gathered around and the blessing given. But at least she was the first to be finished, and before Father had started on his stately walk to the office, she went down the steps and was on her way to school. The sky was clear, but the wind blew hard, and she pulled her coat tightly about her.

Emily liked March, liked the wind blowing against her face and legs. It was wide and clean, and smelt of spring. March was a tall

28

town crier with puffed cheeks and purple shoes, heralding the springtime. She hurried to keep up with him.

The village streets were nearly empty at this hour. It was too early for housewives to be abroad, and the smaller children had already gone to school. The elm-bordered walks were swept clear of any speck of dust, the frame houses stood prim and neat behind hedge or picket. What would Amherst be like without those hedges and white fences? Emily wondered. She couldn't imagine. They seemed to stand for privacy and protection from the world that might wish to pry. And Father must have both hedge and fence around his home, a house of brick instead of frame, a house of many wings and chimneys, of strength and solidity, that looked with dignity at the streets down which she was walking.

There, in the house where two tall white urns stood before the door on either side, was where Helen lived. Emily had a sudden impulse to call for her, but that would mean waiting (Helen was forever late), and a few minutes' delay would spoil everything.

She quickened her pace through the town, past Emily Fowler's, past Abby Woods's, past President Hitchcock's white-pillared porch guarded by majestic lions. Now she had reached the busy section of town and the two emporiums whose latticed windows reflected the morning sunlight in a dazzling myriad of golden squares. Before one of them stood Deacon Luke Sweetser, town merchant, a neighbor and rival of Squire Dickinson. They were rivals in the matter of fast horses, but true and loyal neighbors in everything else. His ruddy face, bucolic as a Baldwin apple, beamed at the sight of Emily's slight figure speeding along on the wind. He put out a chunky hand to stop her. 'Whoa, there, my young friend! At this rate, you'll outstrip your father's horses. — Not that it wouldn't be a simple task!' He chuckled over his barb at the Squire's mares.

'Shall I tell him so, Deacon Sweetser?' Emily stopped to ask. She loved to foster the spirit of competition between these two.

'Why not? Ed'ard needn't think he can always have the swiftest runners in this town. Tell you what, I'm buying two new horses — prizewinners — before Cattle Show next fall. We'll see whether your father can hold to his record then.' His good-natured grin widened at the prospect of a race.

Emily's soul danced with mischief. 'I have only one request,' she told him.

'What is that?'

'Let me play Jehovah to the contest and judge the winner.'

Luke Sweetser raised his eyebrows; Ed'ard's daughter had a wild tongue in her head, no doubt of it. 'Play Jehovah,' indeed! But he enjoyed her for it and consented now with a vigorous nod of his head. 'So be it. If a race is run, you shall be judge.'

'Good, that's a promise, now. Don't forget.' They shook hands like conspirators, and then Emily bade him good-bye. 'I want to get to school early, and I won't make it unless I fly.' She had already wasted several minutes. She glanced back up Main Street and saw other students beginning to come in groups of two or three. There was not much time left if she intended to see Miss Adams before anyone came.

The stores were on one side of the common, the Academy and College on the other. As she crossed over toward the white stone building that housed the Academy, the agitation rose in her veins. What would Miss Adams say to her secret? She only hoped the teacher would be alone!

The classroom was still empty when she went in. Miss Adams sat with her fair head bent over the copy-books on her desk. Emily approached shyly. Now she was here, she hardly knew what to say. She pulled a roll of foolscap from under her arm and held it out. 'Miss Adams . . .'

'Why, Emily Dickinson!' The teacher looked up with pleasure. 'How nice to see you back! Is your cold quite gone?'

'Yes, thank you. I'm fine now.' Emily fingered the roll of paper. 'Miss Adams, here are some compositions I wrote. I didn't care to get behind in my work.'

30

The young woman smiled. 'Emily, I don't think that would be possible! You're way ahead now. But I'm glad to have these new pieces' — she started undoing the roll — 'and I know the class will be, too. We've missed your wit, my dear.'

'Oh, thank you, Miss Adams!' A word from this lovely young tutor meant more than a load of praise from other instructors. Now was the time to ask her opinion! 'Miss Adams, do you think I . . . that is . . .' She hesitated, unable to go on suddenly.

'Yes, Emily? What is it?'

'Well, do you think I . . . am old enough to read the new books?' she finished in a rush. Somehow, she wasn't able to tell Miss Adams what she had found out yesterday. It wasn't time to tell anyone yet until she was sure of it herself.

'What sort of books do you mean?'

'Some of those by Mr. Longfellow and Mrs. Childs?'

Again Miss Adams smiled. 'Emily, I think you had better wait a few years before trying to read the literature of our day. You're just learning to swim, you know. Stay in safe water a while longer.'

Emily wanted to hear more, but the classroom was beginning to fill up, and Emily Fowler, along with Helen Fisk and some others, beckoned her to come and sit beside them.

'Emily, how good to have you back!' 'Are you well now?' 'Don't get sick again, Emily, or we shall die of boredom!' They fell upon her, they were all so happy to see her.

'What did I tell you?' said Helen triumphantly. 'I told her how much we all missed her!'

But Miss Adams was rapping for order, and they had to stop. There was grammar drill, followed by oral reading of compositions. Miss Adams chose one at random from the pile on her desk. 'Willy Lester,' she read. 'Come up and deliver your composition, please.'

An ungainly youth with an unusually long head, and arms and legs that dangled a mile out of his clothes, shuffled laconically up to the platform, while the class sighed audibly in disgust. It would have to be Willy, just on the day Emily Dickinson returned, and they were all waiting to listen to one of her lively papers again!

'Think Twice Before You Speak,' rasped Willy, in a voice resembling a nutmeg grater. He straightened the sheets elaborately, cleared his throat, and began.

It went on and on. There was no end to the theme, read in dull, halting, rasping speech by its writer. The class exchanged glances and stifled its groans. Emily and Helen nudged each other unceasingly, remembering what Emily had said the day before about Willy's compositions. Suddenly Emily took up her pencil, and wrote in large letters on the back of a drill sheet: 'He had better think twice before *he* speaks!' and held it up for all near-by her to see.

There was a titter around her that the girls couldn't hold back. It was so funny!

Miss Adams glanced in the direction of the disturbance, but Emily's face was calm and innocent, her eyes gazing dreamily out of the window. The others were still trying to smother their giggles.

'Girls,' the teacher reproached them, 'Willy has not written a humorous composition, and I see nothing to laugh at. If something has struck you as being funny, let the rest of us know, or exercise your self-control. You would do well to take the attitude of your serious neighbor, Emily Dickinson.'

At her last words, riot threatened as the girls struggled to keep from bursting into uproarious laughter. With many contortions and grimaces they somehow managed to settle down, while Emily watched them as someone who had no part in the proceedings and only the suggestion of a twinkle in her red-brown eyes betrayed the fact that she had been the instigator.

Willy resumed his lecture, and when it was finally over, class was dismissed.

Emily left the Academy building and went over to the College library in search of something she might be allowed to take home with her. Only a limited number of books was permitted to leave the library each day. Leonard Humphrey, the librarian, his deeply sunken eyes glued to the volume in his hands, his lean legs curled around the supports of the desk chair, did not hear her come softly in at the library door. Only when she stood before him, her slight figure casting a shadow over the page, did he raise his eyes to see what was obscuring the light.

'Emily Dickinson,' he said then, with his slow smile. 'I might have known! You are the first student to come in today. You may have your choice.' One lean arm, clad in a sleeve pulled and patched at the elbow, went out toward the bookshelves in a grand gesture.

'Thank you, sir.' Emily made him a deep curtsy, and they both laughed. 'But will you choose one for me?' she asked, more seriously. 'I'm never sure which one I should take.'

The young man stood up and ran his hand through his rather stringy, muddy-colored hair till it stood on end. He walked the length of the shelves and finally removed a book, blowing the dust from the top of it as he returned. As librarian and part-time student at Amherst College, Leonard Humphrey spent many more hours in reading and studying than in caring for the books that comprised the small library.

'Here is one you should like,' he smiled down at her dimly. He was always remote, as if he were peering at her from another world.

'Thank you.' Emily looked at the title. It was *The Lady of the Lake*, by Sir Walter Scott. 'Oh, I know I shall like it!' she exclaimed. 'Will you excuse me if I go now? Perhaps I can read a little before geology class begins.'

'Run along.' He opened the door for her. 'But first you must promise to come in and tell me your thoughts when you've finished.'

'Of course I will. That's part of reading.' And she was off down the walk.

Leonard Humphrey watched her go with admiration in his hazy eyes. If there were more scholars like Emily Dickinson, he thought, they would not dream of barring females from institutions of higher learning.

33

The study of geology included a course in botany, and today they were going to study some trailing arbutus the professor had found under the snow. Emily loved the small, pink, aromatic flower and she couldn't bear to think of tearing it apart to count the stamens. Much as she liked botany, she always dreaded dissecting the flowers. She loved them all and felt it was like murdering them.

The blossoms rested in a bowl on the laboratory table, and she thought they were far too beautiful to touch. So she began to ask questions of Mr. Taylor. In what other parts of the world did they grow? Why were they so delicately colored? How could they blossom under the snow?

He answered everything in close detail, and then launched into a lecture on the wonders of God and the glory of Creation, in keeping with the principles of the Academy. Emily listened to his words, thinking all the while, 'As long as he talks, we won't do any dissecting, we won't hurt them.' She was sure flowers had lives like humans and that they had souls and became immortal after they wilted.

Mr. Taylor was now so engrossed in the subject of wild flowers that he continued talking, and his enthusiasm led him into other topics. He suggested that the pupils start herbariums, collections of wild flowers, and he gave directions for preserving the plants.

He was carried along by a steady flow of ideas until the class was over, and there was no time for laboratory work. 'We shall dissect the arbutus at the next session,' he said, dismissing the class; 'day after tomorrow.'

'And by then,' thought Emily with satisfaction, 'they'll be wilted, and won't care what we do!' She chuckled to herself. You could always get Mr. Taylor off the track with a question or two.

The timid little man stopped her as she passed the desk. 'Do you think you would be interested in starting a small herbarium?' he asked.

'Oh, yes, Mr. Taylor!' Emily felt she must be enthusiastic, since she had led him onto the subject.

'I have some pictures here somewhere.' He began rummaging through a vast pile of papers in the desk drawer, scattering them, increasing the confusion tenfold. But at last he drew forth some faded prints showing several noted collections. 'Here we are,' he said happily, putting them into her hands.

Several of the girls crowded around to look, exclaiming over the pictures, and craning their necks to see. 'Let's all start one!' suggested Abiah, a tall, fair girl who wore spectacles. And in a burst of enthusiasm, they all agreed.

They spoke of nothing else for weeks, it was always that way when a fad or hobby struck them. Yet the days passed, and Emily, who had begun it all, could not find time to join in. There was always so much to do at home, to study, to read, to write about in compositions, besides the housework and gardening. There did not seem to be a moment for outside activities, and two months went by before she was able to enter into this one, along with the rest of the girls. It was near the end of the term, when the birds had flown back to Amherst, and the countryside was a sea of green once more, that Emily set off one afternoon to hunt wild plants for the herbarium she had finally started. On her arm was a small basket containing a garden trowel, and as she moved swiftly down the familiar paths to the woods, it jiggled and bounced against the basket sides.

Every inch of ground in the woods was home to Emily, she had walked there so often. She knew exactly where to turn for the first wild flowers of spring, going straight to them as if by instinct. Now she headed for a bank of ferns and carefully removed two of the plants with her trowel. These she stowed in her basket and began to look about for bloodroot or hepatica. She found plenty of the first and put several of them in beside the ferns. She discovered some green velvety moss which she added to the collection.

Still not seeing any hepatica, she turned off and headed deeper into the woods. It was still and warm with none but the forest voices to break the peaceful quiet. Emily was glad she had come alone. At school Helen had wanted to come along, but much as Emily liked her, she was afraid her friend might spoil the mystery and make-believe that lay hidden in the woods. Vinnie's company, too, had been refused. She had to be alone in the dim, leafy silence, or the pretend was gone from it, the feeling of being part of the woods and of the many little creatures that inhabited it.

> The bee is not afraid of me,
> I know the butterfly;
> The pretty people of the woods
> Receive me cordially.

The lines were there, not in so many words — that would come later — but like an unsung song that hummed through her mind on afternoons like this, when she was wandering by herself.

On and on she went. She stopped once to watch an oriole deftly add a string to its low-hanging nest, and again to notice just how the bees removed the pollen from the cups of flowers. During the operation she scarcely dared move a muscle or the bee would fly off and hover just above the petals until she moved away or became still again.

At last she saw the frog pond she had been heading for, smooth as glass, studded with green lily pads where the little green fellows sunned themselves and sang in deep voices. Splash! splash! As she came to the edge of the pond, the frogs went down into the water to hide until all was quiet again and they could climb out once more to blink sleepily at Emily.

She laughed and blinked back at them. How nice to be a frog and sit upon a pad and sing all day long!

She saw some marsh marigolds near the bank, and underneath, almost hidden, some hepatica was growing. The search had ended. Taking up her trowel, Emily removed the plant that had blossoms on it, pale blue flowers covered with fine hairs, that peeped out shyly from the big leaves. What a fine addition to the herbarium!

36

Having deposited her cargo in the basket, she sat down on a large flat stone to dream awhile before going home. The sun was slowly sinking in the west, but she scarcely noticed its descent, and it was not until the shadows began to lengthen out over the pond and the frogs set up their nightly croaking that she suddenly realized it must be growing late. She would have to hurry! Catching up her basket and trowel, she skirted the edge of the pond and retraced her steps toward home. With feet that barely touched the ground she ran through the woods until she reached the meadow, across which she went more slowly, in case Father should be at home and be displeased to see her come tearing across the field.

She walked as fast as she dared, crossed the road to the white picket fence, and hurried inside the gate. There was no one around. She went to the side door, and after depositing her basket by the steps, slipped quietly in. Austin was standing near-by, and Emily glanced anxiously at the clock on the shelf above his head.

'Austin, is it late? What time is it?' Her voice was close to a whisper.

'Can't you tell yet, Emily?'

'I'm never sure.' She shook her head. 'I only know the sun is beginning to set.'

'It's a quarter past six.'

'Then Father is home!'

Austin nodded. 'And here's Mother.'

For once their mild little mother was heated and emphatic. 'Emily, Emily, where have you been? Vinnie and I searched all over for you. And look at you!' Mrs. Dickinson clacked her tongue in dismay as she noticed Emily's grass-stained clothes, and the hardened half-rings of mud on her fingernails. The girl was a regular minx!

'I just went to the woods, Mother; I needed plants for my herbar . . .'

But Emily got no farther, for her mother interrupted in a great hurry: 'Well, go and change your clothes and wash your hands immediately. Your father is home already, and it is your night to set the table!' She wished Emily would show more responsibility toward the household. It was time the girl stopped day-dreaming.

Emily had completely forgotten the duty which was hers that day. It was a strict rule that the girls alternate in setting the table every day, and neither one was allowed to skip a turn. If she happened to be late, the dining-room held an empty board until the task was done by the one who was supposed to perform it.

Up the steps Emily fled to her room, catching a glimpse of Father deep in his paper in the library. Her fingers flew as she unbuttoned her pinafore and frock, and donned the freshly starched ones Mother had laid out on the bed.

A few minutes later, clean and well-brushed, she was in the pantry, getting down the blue plates. One of them was nicked around the edge, and Father, having found it at his place several times, had issued an order not to use it again.

But Emily was in too much of a hurry now to notice which ones she was taking down. She whisked from pantry to table, and back again once, twice, three times, fetching and carrying plates, silver, and tumblers to set on the white cloth Mother had laid.

At last it was finished, somewhat sketchily, to be sure, but everything was on. Father was summoned, and the whole family sat down. With bowed heads they listened to the blessing which came from the head of the table in a deep voice. But only a word or two had been uttered when Emily realized from Father's tone that something was wrong. Was it because she had been late? Because the napkins were a little crooked, and the spoons stuck out slantwise at Austin's place? Still, you could hardly notice it.

The blessing ended in a deadly quiet, all of them sensing disapproval in the air. Finally Father spoke, the words crashing like thunder: 'Who set the table tonight?'

Suddenly Emily saw what was wrong; she had taken the chipped plate down by mistake and had given it to Father, of all people!

'Lavinia?' came the accusation.

38

Vinnie shook her head, not daring to speak.

'I did, Father.' Emily's voice rang clear.

'You did.   Well, have we not enough ware in this household that we must use cracked and battered plates, fit for the trashpile?' He picked up the round blue disk and held it before Emily.

She did not answer. With blazing eyes she snatched it from his fingers, to the astonishment of all. What would Father do now? Austin held his breath, Vinnie kept her eyes on her locked hands, trembling, and Mother turned from Father to Emily as they stood glaring at one another.

'You shan't be bothered with it again!' cried Emily, and she went running from the room.

Through the little back hall, through the pantry, through the kitchen she ran, never stopping till she was out of the house and back behind the woodpile. Then, raising the troublesome dish above her head, she hurled it to the ground, where it broke in a thousand pieces.

'Smashed!' she exclaimed with satisfaction. She stayed for some moments gazing at the shattered porcelain, and then decided to go back, though somewhat fearful of what Father would have to say.

As it turned out, he said not a word. He merely looked at her in cold silence as she returned to her place, and Emily noticed he had an unmarred plate. Everyone was eating silently, and Mrs. Dickinson stated calmly: 'We thought it best not to wait, Emily. Now please eat your dinner.'

But Emily had a hard time swallowing her food, for she knew Father would not speak to her again for some time, and this punishment was always harder for her to bear than any other. Somehow the meal was finally ended, and Emily went up to her room to avoid her father's cold behavior toward her.

For two days he spoke not a word to her, and they were sad days for Emily. She would rather take a whipping than be completely ignored this way. If only Father would say something, even to scold her! This was the longest estrangement from him she had ever known.

Around sundown on the second day, Emily was trailing through the hall forlornly on the way up to her room, her only comfort when everything was twisted, when she heard Father calling to her from the library. He had just come in a short while before, and still held his hat and cane.

'Emily,' he asked, 'suppose you and I take a little walk before dinner?'

The punishment was over! And Emily knew from past experience the subject of the plate would never be mentioned again. With a glad little cry, she ran to get her bonnet.

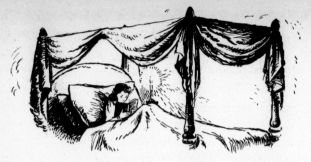

CHAPTER FIVE

I T WAS ON THIS WALK that Emily first learned of Father's great plan for Amherst.

'Do you see that line of woods back of Professor Tyler's and over toward Belchertown?' he asked, pointing it out to her with his cane.

'Yes?' said Emily, wondering.

'Well, Emily . . .' Father paused, as if not quite sure whether to tell her or not, 'if I can overcome the opposition, and if all goes well, there will be a railroad running just beyond those woods between Amherst and Belchertown.' He stopped to see the effect of this statement on his favorite child, for though they might have bitter and fiery clashes, it was Emily in whom the Squire took most pride and who somehow seemed closest to him.

'A railroad, here!' she breathed in astonishment. 'Father, do you think it could really be? Amherst is only a village, so far from the busy centers . . .'

'But that's why we must bring it here, child! To lessen the distance, to speed the travel. Why, it will put Amherst on the map!' His voice beat with excitement, his eyes went beyond her as he pictured the fulfillment of this dream of his.

So, thought Emily, Father has dreams, too, not like mine, but dreams all the same. 'Do you really think it will go through?' she asked.

'If we work hard enough, and fight hard enough. There'll be those who will oppose it. Naturally, there always are. But I'm prepared to fight them, no matter how many there are!'

'And you'll win, too!' predicted Emily with pride. How strong Father was, how determined when he set out to do something! He had already put the College on the map, and the finest thinkers in the country wanted to come there to teach now.

'Thank you, Emily.' He gave her one of his rare, brief smiles. 'With you and the others behind me, I know I can't fail. But there's going to be a battle, make no mistake about that.'

'I know.'

'But we won't say anything about it for a while, even at home,' he went on. 'I shall have to get permission to draw up the plans first, and then I must present them to the elders of the village. It may take some time.'

'I've locked my lips.' Emily turned an imaginary key on her mouth, and smiled at her father. She felt proud to think that he had confided his project to her long before anyone else knew.

He met her eyes for a moment with a deep, penetrating glance, grateful for her understanding, but reserved, and wondering, as always, what went on in her young brain. 'We had best go back now,' he said, taking her hand. 'They'll be waiting dinner.'

It was nearly two years before the dignitaries of Amherst received their first view of Father's plans, but for Emily the months sped swiftly by, there was so much going on every minute of the time.

Austin frequently brought his friends home from the Academy, and she and Vinnie would bring theirs. In this way they formed many lively gatherings. Sometimes they went sleigh-riding, sometimes driving; sometimes they had literary club meetings where they talked of poetry and great writing and new thought. They went to 'handed teas,' and gave them. There were many guests coming and going at the Dickinsons' all the time.

And all the while the secret locked in Emily's innermost being grew and swelled and threatened to burst the bonds she had set upon it. But she kept it rigidly to herself, scarcely letting it outside her mind and feeding it with constant thought on one subject or another.

After their walk on that memorable day, she also thought a great deal about Father. Behind the stern exterior, Emily felt sure he was a man who loved beauty and knew how to laugh, though he never would have admitted it. He was a man of vision, too. Besides the railroad, he was beginning to talk about freeing the slaves in the South and about going to war if it became necessary. The war might never have to be, but there were angry mutterings in both the North and South, and men like the Squire felt that the storm must break sometime.

Emily dwelt upon these important activities of Father in the privacy of her own room and felt her respect for him grow deeper every day. A good part of her time was spent in thinking about those she knew and loved, discovering the real value in different people.

And of course, there were books — she couldn't stop thinking about them. There were many books in the library downstairs. They lined the walls from floor to ceiling, but they were mostly law texts, musty old tomes, or the standard collections of the classics thought proper to read. Father would not allow his children to have the new books that were being written, although Emily was burning for the sight of the latest editions.

Maybe Ben Newton would help her get her hands on some. Ben was the young man who had recently come to study in Father's law office, and he thought young people ought to study the new literature. He wasn't afraid to stand up for his ideas, either. The way he would enter into a discussion with Deacon Sweetser or the Squire on Sunday afternoons at tea, sticking to his arguments through the fire and brimstone of the older men, delighted Emily and Austin. They always hoped some 'question' would arise when he came to call.

43

She felt that Ben would understand. Slender, with a long, thin face and long, thin hands, he was both quiet and amusing, ready for fun, but steadfast in his beliefs. 'Read everything you can,' he had told Emily, 'and then think about what you've read a long time, till it becomes yours. Don't come to any conclusions till you've studied the facts, but once you've made a decision, have the courage to stick to your convictions. And from your chin,' he added, smiling, 'I don't think you'll have any difficulty in doing so.'

Emily laughed. 'Mother says I'm as stubborn as Father sometimes.'

Ben laughed, too, but he went on more seriously, 'And don't be afraid to dream, Emily.'

She was startled. 'How could you tell?'

'It shines out of your eyes like starlight all the time.'

'It's true, I do have "re-ve-ries," as Father calls them,' Emily admitted, but she didn't say any more, not just then.

'And you must go on having them,' Ben encouraged her. 'Great cities have been built on dreams, and monuments erected to them.'

Emily was thinking of this conversation one early fall day when the weather was still warm and the leaves outside her bedroom window showed the first tints of rusty red. 'Ben means that thoughts are like towers and great buildings,' she mused, 'and that they are honored down through the ages. Imagine any of my thoughts being honored down through the ages!' That was a dream! And a fantastic one!

She put it from her mind as a low whistle came to her ears from the downstairs hall. It was Austin, home from class. She ran to meet him.

'Look!' He held out a book. 'It's the new one by Longfellow called *Kavanagh*.'

'Oh!' Emily opened her eyes wide. 'Where did you get it? Let's see!' She was just about to examine it, when they heard the side door click.

'It's Father!' said Austin. 'What'll I do with it?'

44

'Here!' Emily lifted the cover of the old-fashioned square piano and thrust the book underneath. It was safely hidden when Father walked in a moment later.

'Good day, children,' he greeted them solemnly, even more solemnly than usual. He looked strangely tired and strained.

'Good day, Father,' replied Emily and Austin.

What could the trouble be, Emily wondered. The Squire's face wore an expression almost of defeat. It was hard to imagine Father ever being defeated by anything.

Mother and Vinnie came in from the kitchen, and they all went into the dining-room for their midday meal. The others, too, noticed that all was not well with the head of the family.

Mrs. Dickinson tried to make a little conversation to take his mind from his worries. 'Did you see, dear,' she said, 'the thermometer stands just at seventy.' She had a little thermometer in the dining-room window and always consulted it when there was nothing else to say. 'Isn't that warm for this time of the year?'

Her husband nodded without speaking, and the storm remained on his face. At last it broke with a full impact on them all, for the Squire had long since mentioned his plans to the family as well as to Emily. 'I presented the plan for the railroad to the elders of the village this morning,' he announced in tragic tones.

This was momentous news. 'What did they say?' His family leaned forward eagerly. 'Will it go through? When will they begin work?'

He shook his head. 'They turned the idea down flat.'

It couldn't be; the Squire had never been turned down by anyone! They sat silent and astonished.

Emily was the first to speak. 'But why?' she demanded indignantly. 'What did they say?'

'They scoffed at the whole plan of a railroad between Amherst and Belchertown. They called it impossible and absurd! "Who will pay for laying the tracks? Who will pay for the cars? Who will

45

ride in the cars? The stagecoach is fast enough for anyone!" That was the way they answered me!" He was angry, but he was downcast, too. The refusal had been a great blow to him.

He looked around the table when he finished his recital, mutely asking them for support, but he need not have done so, for their loyalty rose even before his last words.

'You're not going to give up, are you, Father?' asked Austin.

'Of course he isn't!' Emily turned on her brother. She stood up and went over to Mr. Dickinson's chair. 'We're with you, Father. We'll tell those chatter-boxes!' Her eyes were angry sparks.

'Thank you, Emily.' The Squire showed his appreciation with a warm look. He was proud of his daughter's spirit.

'Of course, dear,' murmured Mrs. Dickinson in her gentle manner, 'we shall always stand by anything you undertake.' And Vinnie added, sympathetically, 'They ought to be ashamed, those people!'

'Thank you, all of you.' He looked around at them gratefully. 'It does me good to know how you feel.'

'But isn't there anything you can do, Father?' pursued Emily. 'There must be another way!'

'Well,' he said slowly, 'Sweetser and I could try to form a stock company for the purpose of financing the railroad. But I would have to be the first investor and it means taking a risk . . .'

'It's worth taking a chance, I know it is!' cried Emily. 'Say you'll try, Father! We'll do all we can to help you.'

'You've been a great help already, my dear. You've given me the courage for a fresh start. Now I think you had better finish eating or you'll be late for class.' It was the closest he had ever come to expressing his emotions, and embarrassment made him turn to the business at hand.

Emily went back to her place full of happiness, for there was a new bond between them, and perhaps now Father would understand her better. She picked up the half-eaten slice of brown bread and tried to finish it along with the fresh baked beans that had grown cold on her plate. She was too stirred to eat, though, too moved by indignation and zeal and a fierce loyalty toward Father. She fussed with her food, gulped down a few mouthfuls of milk, and hurried off to class with the others.

The book Austin had brought home with him was completely forgotten in the upheaval. It was not until evening that any of them thought of it.

The family were all sitting in the parlor. The Squire was deep in his paper, and Mrs. Dickinson held her inevitable embroidery hoop. Her hands were like white doves as they moved up and down plying the needle in and out of the damask napkin she was monogramming. This was her hour of peace, in which she could rest and relax while she planned the meals for the coming day. Her thoughts were full of menus which might tickle the Squire's palate and divert him from his vexation. How tired he seemed tonight! Edward was a fine husband, strong, a good provider always, and, she felt, extremely wise in the ways of the world. She was fortunate to be married to a man like Edward.

And the children were coming along all right, too. Emily had been a bit wayward, it was true, but she was beginning to settle down some now. Maybe she would grow into a decorous female, after all. As for the others, there was no cause for concern. Austin was a model son (and anyhow, you didn't have to worry about a boy!), and Lavinia had been a sweet, manageable child from the start.

The heads of the three younger Dickinsons were bent over their books, close to the whale-oil lamps so as to get full benefit of the unsteady glow, and their mother let her serene gaze rest on them with tranquil fondness.

Suddenly the Squire put down his paper and said: 'Emily, I wish you would play for me.'

'I'll be glad to, Father.' Emily looked up and closed her book at once. She was just learning to play, and all she knew was a beginner's piece or two, but Father enjoyed listening to her and she liked to perform for him. She rose and started across the room.

And then she remembered the volume hidden under the piano cover! Would Father notice the bulk sticking out? But there it was, and how could he miss it? Austin, too, had remembered, and was trying to warn her. She felt his unspoken message as she passed his chair, but there was nothing to be done. They exchanged glances of helpless resignation as she sat down and began to play, loud and fast, so that the sound and fury would fill the room, and perhaps remove Father's mind from the piano itself.

She practiced all the little pieces she knew. Mother smiled at her with gentle nods of approval in time with the music. Father listened quietly for some moments, but before she had finished, he got up and walked over to the piano and stood watching her. He stood right where the book lay; his hand was almost on top of it. Emily held her breath. Austin tried to keep his eyes on his algebra, but they kept going over toward the piano.

'One-and-two-and-three-and-four!' Emily counted to herself with relief. It was the end of the last composition in her repertoire, and Father had not uttered a word, nor made a sign of interrupting. Indeed, he didn't seem to notice anything extraordinary about the fit of the cover or her manner of playing tonight. When she took her hands from the keyboard at last, he said, 'Thank you, Emily,' and went into the library, closing the door behind him.

This was a signal to Mother to put down her embroidery. 'It's time for bed, my dears.' She nodded to them, and started up the steps. She wanted to lay out a new comforter for Austin.

As her skirt disappeared around the corner of the landing, Emily and Austin made straight for the concealed book. They brought it out quickly, keeping a watch on the library door.

'I'd better take it to my room, Austin,' whispered Emily.

'Yes,' he agreed. 'I'll read it when you're finished.'

'So will I,' added Vinnie. She was used to being the last in order, she really didn't mind. Austin and Emily were such a wonderful brother and sister!

48

They went upstairs and that night Emily burned a candle a long time, reading on the sly. She had discovered only recently that if she stayed awake till the house was completely quiet, she could light her bedside candle and read or work till it burnt out; not every night, for it made her worn and wan the next day, but sometimes, like this moment when she couldn't wait for morning to come and light the pages for her.

She thought the new book was most exciting. Father would enjoy it if he would only let himself look inside a new book. It was a good thing he hadn't discovered their treasure! Or had he? Emily stopped, wondering. The rise in the piano covering had been unmistakable, he couldn't have helped seeing it. Could he have pretended not to notice? Was it, perhaps, his way of thanking them for this noon, of telling Emily, especially, that he wouldn't 'see' those books she cared so much to read? It was hard to tell, but Emily knew him well enough by now to realize that this would be his way of compromise, of letting her know that she was growing old enough to choose what she wished to read, though he might disapprove of her selections. Yes, they were beginning to understand each other.

She resumed her reading, one turned page fell upon the last quickly and ever more quickly as she went on and on, until her sleep-ladened eyes would keep open no longer. She snuffed out the small yellow beam and slid down among the pillows.

'Emily, dear,' her mother called the next afternoon from the spare room where she was sewing, 'I need a spool of silk. Will you go down to Palmer's for me?'

Emily had just come from the Academy, and she was anxious to finish the story, but the distress in Mother's voice meant the errand must be urgent. 'Sounds like trouble,' she commented, poking her head around the door.

Mrs. Dickinson sat at her sewing-table, surrounded by cloth, cutting shears, patterns. 'It certainly is!' Her silver-thimbled finger rapped the table with a short, decisive click. 'I have my fall shirtwaist all cut out and not a thread to sew it. Nothing matches. Now isn't that a shame?'

'Not only a shame, but a catastrophe,' sympathized Emily. 'But don't fret, you shall have your thread.' She took the sample of bright blue merino Mother put into her hand, and went out again.

She walked slowly down the street, her ever-present curiosity prompting her to look at everything along the familiar way as if she were seeing it for the first time, for it was Emily's particular gift to view all things afresh each day. She came to Brick Row, with all its shops. On a sign outside the livery stable was painted a yellow horse with a fiery red mane. It looked like something the Devil himself might have ridden in on some black night and left behind him in a hurry, but Seth E. Nims, the livery-stable keeper, was extremely proud of it. And there was the huge black dog's head with his gay collar of scarlet and white morocco that advertised the harness-maker's shop. Next came the town's red and white striped barber pole, standing in front of the shop where Amherst's older gentlemen had their hair and beards trimmed. She stopped a moment before the apothecary's alongside it. In the window hung large globes filled with mysterious-looking blue and red liquid, suspended from the ceiling by brass chains. Emily always wondered what the liquids were in those globes. They looked like a witch's mixture.

She came to the hotel across from the common, and looked to see if there was anyone her age among the knots of people clustered there. Today the common was filled with carriages, with men talking business and ladies gossiping. Cattle Show would be in a few days, and all kinds of preparations were being made already. But there were none of her special friends among the busy groups, so she turned into Palmer's, which was right next to the hotel.

She bought the thread for Mother, and when she came out the sun seemed a trifle warm, so she opened a silk parasol she had brought with her and put it over her shoulder, twirling it slowly as she walked back down Brick Row. At Main and Pleasant Streets, she saw a familiar figure come out of Father's office. It was Ben Newton. He waved to her and crossed the street.

'Good afternoon, Emily.' He lifted his high hat of pearl-gray felt.

'Good afternoon, Mr. Newton,' Emily returned.

'How have you been spending the time since I last saw you?'

'Up in the clouds.' Emily pointed the tip of her parasol toward the sky. 'Austin brought a new book home yesterday — *Kavanagh* by Mr. Longfellow. I read till long after everyone was asleep. We hid it under the piano cover till Father wasn't looking.'

'Emily' — Ben pretended to be shocked — 'do you deceive your father?'

'Not deceive.' She shook her head. 'We only spare him. We don't want to hurt his feelings. You know as well as I do how he feels about the writing of our day, and it harries him to think we read it.'

'I know,' Ben nodded.

'He says the new books "joggle the mind" . . . But I like to have my mind joggled,' she added.

Ben laughed. 'So do I, Emily. And though I'm a good many years older than you, we belong to a different generation from your father, you and I — a generation that only now is beginning to think for itself. And it's up to us, particularly you, Emily, to absorb all we can of modern thought. I'll tell you what' — his manner lightened suddenly — 'you know the big syringa bush just outside your front door?'

'Yes,' said Emily.

'When I come for tea Sunday, I'll leave a book hidden under that bush, and when I'm gone, you can go and find it.'

'Good!' She loved nothing better than having secrets and Ben seemed to share this delight as no one else did. They had reached the corner now, and he left her to make a call on a client concerning a deed of land.

On Sunday he came to tea as usual. He talked in quite the usual

51

manner and acted as courteously and was as entertaining as always. But when Mother was handing him a second cup of tea, and Father was deep in a discussion with Deacon Sweetser, Ben looked over at Emily and closed one eye ever so slightly.

When he was gone and the rest of the family had begun their various tasks, Emily slipped out of the front door, and bent down before the syringa bush. There was the book! She pulled it out and, hugging it to her, ran upstairs to her bedroom to read.

After the first page, she was no longer in the corner of the world that was Amherst. She was borne a million miles away on the leaves of the volume in her fingers. Books to Emily were wings with which she soared into space, ships in which she explored the world. As she was to write later:

> There is no frigate like a book
> To take us lands away,
> Nor any coursers like a page
> Of prancing poetry.

Only when the others came up to go to bed did she realize where she was, and that it was time for sleep. She was tired, and Cattle Show began early tomorrow, or she would have relit the candle when quiet settled. As it was, she drifted into a slumber filled with dreams about Mrs. Lydia Maria Child's latest book.

CHAPTER SIX

THE DEW had not yet dried on the morning grass when Emily peeped into the barn the next day and discovered Father already hard at work with Tom, grooming the horses. The Squire prided himself on his fine, spirited mounts. He wouldn't allow anyone to claim faster or more perfect ones, and rivalry ran high every year among the three foremost contestants in the 'exhibition of horses': Deacon Luke Sweetser, Seth Nims, and the Squire.

'Can't I help curry them, Father?' Emily spoke from behind her father's shoulder, where she stood watching.

'Why, Emily!' He started at the sound of her voice. She had come in so quietly he hadn't heard her. 'You know, Daughter, that grooming horses is no labor for a young girl. It would be most unbecoming.'

Emily's eyes gleamed. 'But I would so like to feel I had a part in winning the exhibition, for of course you'll win, Father.' She was mildly poking fun at him, but her manner was demure and respectful.

Squire Dickinson still didn't quite know what to say when Emily ribbed him. He could sense laughter somewhere in her words now, but there was nothing he could put his finger on that was really disrespectful. 'I shall do my best,' he told her, 'but I'm not sure our entries will take first place. Sweetser has purchased some new horseflesh again, I hear.' He finished dryly, with a hint of sarcastic humor that delighted his daughter. This was Father's only game.

'Again?' she echoed eagerly. 'Does that mean we shall be going down the Northampton road after Cattle Show?'

'If we are challenged — yes.'

'We,' her father said. So he took it for granted she would be in on the private and unacknowledged marathon that was run between the Deacon and the Squire every time either of them acquired new steeds. Here was another tie that held them close, for all the difference in their outward lives. She remembered the first time she had played judge of the contest, for Luke Sweetser had kept his promise two years ago. She had accompanied the men, sitting beside her father as 'jedge,' and Sweetser had won that day. It was a disappointment, but the next Cattle Show — a year ago — when her father had bought horses, he had won easily. She remembered how the two men had shaken hands after it was over, and Sweetser had admitted, 'Ed'ard, those are fine horses indeed. Now I'll have to get new ones!'

So now he had them. If he challenged Father today and won, the Squire would soon be in the market for first-rate mares! These two men would play at their intense little game as long as they lived, and Emily experienced a strange thrill at the thought that she was part of it. Not many daughters in Amherst would know if their fathers indulged in horse-racing, much less be invited to be a party to it!

She followed the movements of the Squire's arm as he returned to meticulously combing his horse with long, sweeping strokes down its flank. She remained for some time, fascinated by the rhythm and controlled grace of the semicircles he described in the air each time. In his own peculiar way, he was an artist. She had a sudden impulse to give him a hug from the back because he was kind, though always so serious. But no Dickinson was that unbending. As much as the family loved each other, they scarcely ever showed it. She knew she would embarrass her father if she followed her

54

impulse, so she went back to the house to help Mother with the round rye loaves for the bakery exhibit.

When they finished, it was time to dress. What a beautiful fall day! Emily looked out as she changed her clothes.

> The maple wears a gayer scarf,
> The field a scarlet gown.
> Lest I should be old-fashioned,
> I'll put a trinket on.

And she fastened a gold locket around her throat.

Cattle Show, like all other events in Amherst, was held on the Village Green or common. Emily loved the color and gaiety of it. There were military bands playing lively music. There were exhibition matches of all sorts and a display of splendid farm animals. She stood with Ben Newton and Austin beneath the platform at one end of the common, waiting for the events to begin.

'Nothing else is like Cattle Show!' she exclaimed. 'It makes you see how rich the earth is.'

'Yes,' agreed Ben. 'We don't realize it often enough.'

At that moment Professor Tyler climbed to the platform and gave an address. This was followed by a prayer from the minister offering thanks for the harvest. Cattle Show could now begin. A procession formed at the Amherst House, the military band leading the way with mounted escorts on either side. They proceeded to Hadley road, west of the church, for the first event on the program, the plowing match.

Farmers for miles around entered the plowing match, and excitement ran high to see which one would get his strip of land turned over first and most efficiently. Friends stood on the edge of the field cheering. Sometimes the plow horse, confused by the noise, would stall, and the poor tiller lost out completely. Today the race was very close, with two Sunderland valley farmers finishing their strips almost at the same moment. But the judges declared that one of them had done a better job, and awarded him the ribbon.

55

When that was over, the crowd moved to the west side of the common where draft matches were being held. Next the men had to detach their cattle or horses from a group of animals without disturbing the rest. These contests took great skill and knowledge of animals.

From there Emily and Ben Newton walked over to the displays of baked and cooked foods temptingly arranged on wooden stands. How good it all looked! Emily pointed out Mother's crisp brown loaves. 'Mother puts her heart in them, I believe,' she smiled.

Austin came up beside them. 'I'm going to be a judge some time,' he grinned. 'You have to taste everything!'

At last came the exhibition of horses. It took place over the entire common and overflowed down the Main Street. The Squire, Deacon Sweetser, and Seth Nims sat very straight in their buggies, while their shining steeds stamped and pulled at the taut reins. Squire Dickinson was determined and proud as his showy horses stepped out.

Ben Newton laughed. 'That's one of your father's few faults,' he observed. 'He's just like a schoolboy where his fast horses are concerned.'

'I think it's more a virtue than a fault,' said Emily.

Ben shot her a look from his deep-set eyes. 'How so?'

'It makes him human,' Emily explained. 'If he didn't have a weakness or two, he would be too far above the rest of us.'

'That's true,' agreed Ben. 'And you are a very penetrating young woman.'

Emily laughed at him. 'Come, let's move closer,' she said.

The horses in the exhibition did not race. They were slowly paced up and down the common and all along Main Street. They seemed to catch the spirit of the hour and revealed in every step and turn the thoroughbred ancestry that coursed in their veins.

How high the Squire's mares held their sleek heads! He didn't have to check the rein in the least to keep their necks up. He sat like a statue of Correctness in his customary black broadcloth and glistening black topper, so dignified and proper, but beneath there was unwonted elation, an excitement born of suspense. Emily saw it as he glanced out of the corner of his eye at Luke Sweetser, resplendent in a new embroidered waistcoat (he had a flair for flowered waistcoats) which spread over his broad girth like a meadow made of cloth. Edward Dickinson was trying to gauge the worth of his neighbor's horses by their master's confidence, and the smile on the big, good-natured face must have cost him many anxious moments. On the other side, Seth Nims drove his black stallions with equal reliance on their merits for the coveted first place.

Though these three stars shone with outstanding brilliance, there were many displays worthy of attention, and the exhibition lasted some time. Mrs. Dickinson, from her post in the Sweetser carriage, watched the maneuvers with burning interest. She was sure the Squire must win; but still you never knew.

She turned to Mrs. Sweetser who sat beside her. 'Your husband has some excellent beasts — excellent,' she offered politely.

'Thank you,' her neighbor accepted with a benign smile. 'He paid an excellent price for them, let me tell you! I expect him to win this year.'

'He won't if my Edward can help it,' declared Mrs. Dickinson with proper loyalty, and the two ladies indulged in moderate laughter over their husbands' battle. But the next moment they leaned forward in the seat with bristling eagerness, for the judge had come to the front of the platform. After much deliberation on the stance of these, the shoulders or flanks of those, the heads or manes of others, a decision had finally been reached.

The trumpets blew, the crowd waited: 'The first place' — the judge paused dramatically — 'has been awarded to Squire Dickinson's mares and Deacon Sweetser's bays. Both of these entries are equal in merit.'

A tie! A tie! It was a most unusual outcome. The crowd seethed with sensation as Deacon Sweetser drove his horses abreast the Squire's, and the two men shook hands in congratulation. Their lips moved, but few heard what was said.

Emily knew without listening, and she said to Ben: 'Now we shall have a merry time! This will only fan the flame.'

'Emily, you look like a little demon incarnate,' Ben accused her. 'What piece of roguery are you up to now?'

'Nothing, indeed. I assure you whatever takes place is none of my doing.' That, anyway, was the truth.

'Oh, come, aren't you going to let me in on the fun?' he begged.

'I'm sorry.' She shook her head. 'That would mean a betrayal.'

With the exhibition of horses, Cattle Show was over, and the crowd began to disperse. Emily hurried home to be there when Father arrived after reckoning the Cattle Show accounts with members of the committee.

Just before supper he came home. Mrs. Dickinson greeted him with timid gaiety. 'Just imagine, Edward, you and the Deacon both won. Whoever would have thought of a tie?'

'Yes — well, the unexpected is likely to happen any time, my dear.' The Squire had his thoughts on the more pressing matter of a race. 'Emily' — he spoke rather loudly for him — 'Sweetser and I have a little business to take care of on the Northampton road. Would you care to ride with me?'

'Thank you, Father, I should like it very much.' Emily kept her face as straight as her father's. 'I'll be ready in a trice!' She went up to get a warm wrap, for the autumn days grew chill early, and there would be a high draft around the carriage if the two men drove at their customary speed.

'Shall you be late, Edward?' inquired Mrs. Dickinson as Emily and her father left the house.

'No, my dear.' Again there was a note in the Squire's voice not entirely serious. 'I am sure this business will be dispatched with the utmost speed.'

Mrs. Dickinson caught the merest ripple of her daughter's low laughter as she closed the door. Now what, she thought to herself,

58

did Emily find so funny in that remark? She shook her head as she watched the two drive off. The girl was certainly much closer to Edward than to her, in spite of their frequent tilts. But Emily was so unusual, perhaps it was better that way. A father, especially a wise one like the Squire, was better fitted for the guidance of a girl like Emily than a wife and mother, who knew so little of life. Mrs. Dickinson went complacently toward the kitchen to see about supper.

Meanwhile, the two in the carriage found their neighbor waiting for them around the first bend.

Deacon Sweetser was full of good-natured cheerfulness. 'We may've tied at the exhibition, Ed'ard Dickinson,' he called out, 'but it'll be a different story on the road.'

'No doubt of it.' The Squire's meaning was clear, and Luke Sweetser roared appreciatively.

'Emily,' he asked, 'are you ready to judge us once again?'

Emily nodded in high glee, and the two men pulled their horses in an even line. 'One, two, three — go!' cried Emily, and they were off in the direction of Northampton as fast as their horses could run.

This was a thrill well worth waiting for. Emily clung to the seat with both hands and reveled in every second of it. Down the road sped the two carriages, each trailing its cloud of dust. Faster, faster they went, until the Squire's jaw jutted out nearly to the dashboard in determination, and Deacon Sweetser had replaced his cheerful look with grimness, his confidence with something close to belligerence.

Both men were deadly serious now, and neither one would give way by an inch. They were more than halfway to the Northampton outskirts already, yet neither contestant showed a sign of dropping behind in the neck-and-neck dash for supremacy. They rushed along side by side, so close that the manes of the inside horses blew against each other. The deafening beat of hooves was echoed in Emily's ears like the boom of kettledrums. Was this going to prove a tie, too? She closed her eyes, dreading to look at the road.

59

Some moments later she opened them, unable to contain herself. Still neck and neck, they were approaching the end now. She could see the grove of willow saplings along the creek just outside of Northampton — the finish line. They were nearly there!

Suddenly she saw her father edge forward in the seat, ready for a final push. With restrained excitement he lifted his whip, which he used rarely and judiciously, and flicked the rumps of his mares with smart, light lashes, just enough to give them a final spurt of energy.

It was a deft, masterful touch and his horses responded. In the last lap they shot forward, passed the Deacon's bays, and streaked across the line at least a head in front of their opponents.

Emily stood up in her place. 'The winner!' she called out. The two men pulled on the reins and the runners came to a halt, snorting and stamping. Both rivals got down and met in the road.

'Ed'ard,' groaned the Deacon as they shook hands, 'you'll keep me strapped buying new horses!'

The Squire wore an air of triumph, but he refrained from boasting. 'Better luck next time, Deacon,' he said quietly. Both men were short of breath and both made an effort to conceal their emotion by an outward calm.

Emily, as usual, felt sorry for the loser now that it was all over. She smiled over at the other carriage, whose owner was climbing back inside somewhat dejectedly. Even his flowered waistcoat had a wilted appearance.

They drove home slowly, letting the horses regain their wind. As the sun sank behind the Pelham Hills, Emily watched her father's grave eyes grow peaceful with satisfaction. Once again he had proved that his were the fastest horses in town. 'I expect Father will always win,' she thought. 'He has such faith in his horses.'

CHAPTER SEVEN

I T'S SUCH PERFECT AUTUMN WEATHER, let's go to the woods, Em-i-ly!' It was Helen Fisk calling to her as she came from the library a few days after Cattle Show.

'All right.' Emily was always ready for a jaunt in the woods. 'But I have to stop at home and tell Mother we're going.'

'Oh, bother!' Helen was impatient to be off.

'It's just that she worries if we don't report at home after school,' Emily explained apologetically. 'You know how frail my mother is. I don't like to trouble her.'

'Well, my folks certainly would never worry about me!' laughed Helen. She crinkled her button nose so that the tiny freckles across the bridge disappeared for a moment and then popped out again, a match for the brown flecks in her green eyes. She was so alive, spilling over with impulsive action. Sometimes Emily was annoyed by Helen's ever-present enthusiasm, her 'bubbliness,' but you couldn't help loving her.

The girls stopped for Emily Fowler on the way, and the three of them set off at a brisk pace toward the Mansion.

'I won't be a minute,' promised Emily as she went up the steps to the gate.

Mrs. Dickinson was never sure of Helen's reliability. 'Don't let her talk you into anything unreasonable,' she warned Emily.

'Do you think anyone could?' Emily put in.

'And don't forget to be home in plenty of time,' her mother went on. 'I'm not anxious to explain where you are to Father!'

'I know,' nodded Emily. 'Don't worry, Mother, I won't be late.'

So they were on their way at last, three young girls whose dresses had recently been let down to a point where the full skirts swished against the tops of their high shoes, a delicious sensation, for it meant they were nearly young ladies. They chattered and laughed as they swung along back of the village toward the patches of brilliant color the woods made, like daubs of paint against the clear blue sky. It was warm and still, as though Nature were taking a final rest before pushing on toward winter — the suspended season called Indian summer.

Emily's heart was near to bursting at the sight of the turning trees. 'Just look at the Pelham Hills! They've put on their brightest pinafores, a final fling before they say good night.'

'You make them come to life, Em,' said Emily Fowler admiringly.

'Yes,' laughed Helen. 'You'd think she was talking about someone we knew.'

Emily turned on the others with mild astonishment. 'But of course, we know them well!' She wished she had not spoken. Even her closest friends did not always share her ability for making all things animate. It did seem to her that the trees took off their clothes when summer was done.

> Frequently the woods are pink,
> Frequently are brown;
> Frequently the hills undress
> Behind my native town.

Stanzas like this seemed to form subconsciously in Emily's mind, though she did not write them down at once. Until the day when she could come forth with the finished product, everything was grist to her insatiable mill.

'Thorn apples! I see thorn apples and black walnuts!' Helen

64

sang out as they neared the woods. 'I'm going to gather an apron-ful.' And off she flew toward her find.

Emily Fowler preferred wild flowers. 'I'm going to take home an immense bouquet for the big green urn in front of the fireplace. I'll want a little of everything. Now what do you call this, Em?'

She sought Emily for the names — sumac, wild asters, ironweed, goldenrod — such knowledge was second nature to Emily Dickinson. 'I want to find a fringed gentian if I can' — she began searching the spot they had entered. 'We may have to hike a good long way to see one, but the reward will be worth it.'

She led the other two deeper into the woods — not without protest from Helen, whose apron was bulging by this time. 'This is a heavy load,' she complained. 'I can't lug it along for miles and miles.'

Emily laughed at her. 'Maybe we won't go far — and then again perhaps we will,' she teased. 'Why don't you leave some of your booty here?'

'Oh, no! We'll want to eat them. Lead on. I guess I'll make it!' She followed the others with such labored steps that Emily took pity on her, and offered to carry half in her apron. Emily Fowler was laden with her 'immense bouquet.'

They went past creek and marshy bed, over gentle rise and down, winding in and around various groves that might prove likely places to discover a blue gentian. Once Emily had started on the quest, she was indefatigable. For more than an hour she led the way through the corners of the woods.

Helen gave out at last. 'You'll never find one, Emily — let's forget about it. I'm tired.' She plumped down on a log.

'But, Helen, I don't want to stop now. We may be right close to one.'

'Well, let's rest awhile anyhow and get rid of our burden. I'm too weary to drag it another step!'

Emily Fowler was more than willing, so the three made themselves comfortable on logs or grassy plots as they chose. They nibbled lazily at the sweet, bland, woody-tasting little apples as they rested, speaking only occasionally when some thought moved them. Emily found a sharp stone and cracked open the thick-shelled nuts and they savored the rich, tangy kernels.

'This is the life!' sighed Emily Fowler as she leaned back against a tree trunk and breathed in the spicy air. 'This is the life!'

The others did not bother to voice agreement, it was so obvious. Emily closed her eyes and thought, 'She should have omitted one little word, *the*, and then she'd have discovered a truth.'

But after a few minutes, Helen spoke her mind. 'Yes, this is pleasant enough, when you have nothing better to do, but I should hate to think of spending a lifetime in a place that has no more to offer than Amherst!'

'But Amherst — and all this — is home! Don't you love home?' demanded Emily.

'Yes, I suppose so, in a way. But it's so sleepy and dull here — so provincial!' Helen had recently picked up this fashionable term which she liked to flaunt. 'Don't you think it's provincial? I want to see the world.'

'Perhaps the world is provincial, too,' suggested Emily, with a certain dry humor that brought a giggle from Emily Fowler.

But Helen was not disturbed in the least. 'Oh, no — I'm sure the big cities are vastly different from Amherst — think of the activity, the color! Oh, I long to travel, to be worldly! And I mean to do it, too,' she finished with determination. 'Come, be honest, you two. Wouldn't you like to get away from Amherst?'

'Mm, I might enjoy a trip now and then,' said Emily Fowler, 'but I wouldn't want to live anywhere else. I should miss my friends so.'

'You'd meet new friends, new people all the time — worldly, sophisticated people. I think it would be enchanting,' babbled Helen. 'What about you, Em?'

'I don't know. The names of far places fascinate me. I like to read and have reveries of them' — Emily's eyes took on a remote expression — 'but I think, if you look deeply enough, you can see the world in Amherst.'

'What do you mean by that?'

'I don't know.' Emily herself was somewhat surprised at the statement. 'I'll have to think about it.'

'Oh, Emily, you're as deep as the sea and just as mysterious!' exclaimed Helen. 'Well, I intend to leave the very first chance I get. Of course I'll come back to see you from time to time.'

'Shall you be able to get away?' Emily inquired.

'Now and then, I suppose,' Helen began seriously, but the look on Emily's face made her stop. 'You goose! Pulling my leg, weren't you? It's not fair!' With that all three of them started to talk at once and the branches rang with their shouts. 'Come on!' cried Helen, intoxicated by the spirit of raillery, 'let's start at once! We can get the coach to Pelham easily.' She stood up and shook out her apron, the thorn apples rolling over the ground like red marbles. She headed toward the highway outside the woods.

'I can't go.' It was Emily, who had not moved.

'Why not? If we're lucky, we can be there and come back in an hour or so.'

'If we're lucky,' repeated Emily. 'And even though we catch the coach right away, we might be stranded in Pelham for hours. You know how long it takes sometimes till there are enough passengers for the trip.'

'Well, we can take a chance. Do get started, Emily.'

Emily smiled as she thought of her mother's advice. 'Unreasonable' would hardly have been Mrs. Dickinson's word for Helen's latest suggestion. 'I'm sorry, Helen. I don't dare to risk it. Father expects us all to be home when he gets there, and I upset his rule more than the others as it is. Running off to Pelham without leave would be too much of an infraction.'

'Your father is so strict and stern, Emily! I don't see how you bear it!' Helen turned around and came back.

Emily was amazed to hear her description of the Squire. Was

that the way he appeared to outsiders? 'He isn't really "strict" or "stern," Helen,' she protested. 'It's only' — the realization came to her suddenly — 'that he cares for us all so much. He wants us to be perfect, and he doesn't want anything to happen to us.' She was somehow hurt at her friend's hasty indictment of Father. It was all right for her or Austin and Vinnie to criticize, to mock his austere gravity. It was their privilege because they loved him, but no outsider, even Helen, could censure him.

Helen saw that she had spoken too hastily. She sat down beside Emily on the log, instantly contrite. 'Please forget what I said,' she begged. 'I didn't understand. Besides, you ought to know I don't mean half of what I say!'

Emily was forced to. laugh. 'At least you're honest, Helen. It's forgotten. Let's see whether we can find the gentian now.' She stood up, and gave Helen a pull. 'If we go home the other way, I think I know just the spot.'

'Such single-mindedness!' said Emily Fowler. 'Is it much farther?'

'Not at all. Just follow me, I'll show you how to go.' Emily led them homeward through one of the bypaths she had discovered on her solitary trips, pausing now and then to scan the scenery for the rare, fringed blossom. But it was useless, there seemed to be none anywhere.

They were approaching a low hill near the town when she finally saw a flash of the color she had been waiting for. She ran ahead of the others and knelt to examine the flower. Yes, it was really a fringed gentian, a wonderful bluish-purple, with the cap of fringe, like a crown on top.

'See?' she called as the others came up. 'Isn't it beautiful?'

Helen and Emily Fowler admired her treasure, but they couldn't feel the same ecstasy that Emily Dickinson knew for the incomparable in nature. When they had examined it for some moments, Emily rose and started on again.

'Aren't you going to pick it?' asked Helen.

'Of course not! Fringed gentians are too scarce. I wouldn't want to deprive the hillside of this one. It's enough just to see a single specimen.'

'Well, I'm glad you finally found it, anyway.' Helen slipped an arm through hers. 'I don't think you could have slept tonight if you hadn't.'

'That's right,' laughed Emily. 'And I really owe you a vote of thanks for suggesting that we come today.' They smiled at each other; Emily Fowler took her arm on the other side, and they all three moved toward home in unison.

Neither Helen nor Emily Fowler could know how uncommon a sight was the flower they had seen. Only Emily Dickinson, with her lore of the woods, was cherishing its memory:

> God made a little gentian;
> It tried to be a rose
> And failed, and all the summer laughed.
> But just before the snows
> There came a purple creature
> That ravished all the hill;
> And summer hid her forehead,
> And mockery was still.

CHAPTER EIGHT

THE NEXT YEAR, when she was seventeen, Emily went to study at Mount Holyoke Seminary. She had been eager to go away to school, yet, when the day came to leave and Father brought the family carriage to the front door, waiting for her like the stagecoach, she suddenly hated to leave home. What would it be like at the Seminary? How strange it would seem not to wake up in her own room, not to see her family every day, but strange faces and strange rooms! Perhaps the work would be too hard for her. She wished in her heart she could stay at home, but it was too late now. All the arrangements had been made.

Kissing Mother and Vinnie good-bye quickly, she ran down the walk and climbed in the cabriolet. Father lifted the whip, and they were off. Emily leaned out and watched the Mansion grow smaller and smaller as they drove, until at last she could see its spires no longer. She was really going away to stay.

The first few days at Mount Holyoke were terrible ones for Emily. New faces before her all the time — three hundred girls! They seemed like a million. And the entrance examinations, which lasted three solid days, were terrifying. Suppose she didn't pass! She worried and studied all the time between exams.

School was all so different from home. Emily tried to be like the other girls, laughing and talking in the halls, or slipping in to visit in one another's rooms, a practice strictly against the rules.

But she couldn't enter into the spirit, she kept thinking about home. She felt lost without Father, somehow. He was so much a part of every day, it was hard to get used to life without his direction. She missed Vinnie's dear, comforting ways and Austin's readiness for conspiracy, his quiet understanding of her eagerness to learn and to break away from tradition in her thought. She longed for the sight of Mother, always resembling a portrait of a gentle lady, delicate but enduring. She kept remembering, too, the faces of those who so often crossed the threshold of the Mansion — kind Ben Newton, and scholarly Leonard Humphrey (though Leonard, she reflected, wouldn't be there this year as he had gone to Andover), and Emily Fowler, Helen, and some of the others. She could picture it all so clearly that it removed any desire to mingle with the girls here, though most of them were pleasant and amiable.

They were outside the door now, a whole bevy of them on their way to Jerusha Abbott's room down the corridor.

Melissa Usher stuck her round face capped by a ring of braids in at the doorway. 'Won't you two join us?' she asked of Emily and her roommate. 'Jerusha's had a box from home — already!'

Marianne Carter, who shared the small white room with Emily, jumped up at once, her pretty face glowing with enthusiasm. 'Of course, I'm delighted to come! What about you, Emily?'

But Emily shook her head slowly. 'Thank you, I prefer to remain here.'

'You'll never get to know any of the girls if you sit here and mope all the time! Do join us,' Marianne tried to persuade her. 'Many of them are quite nice,' she added, a little hurt. 'Don't you wish our company at all?'

'Of course I do, and I'll come with you one of these days soon.' Emily felt ashamed of herself. She hesitated a moment; how could she make her roommate see why she wasn't more sociable? 'It's just that I have such a very dear home,' she explained at last. 'I can't help thinking about it. But I'll get over it.'

And after the first few days, she did. Her examinations received good marks, and with the rest of the students, she settled down to school life and study.

The Seminary, run by its founder, tall, vibrant Miss Mary Lyon, was brimming over with religious fervor, and the strict rules were in accordance with those of a young ladies' boarding-school in 1847. Girls were not allowed to leave the grounds except at holidays. Visitors were chaperoned by the teachers, and such pastime as the sending of 'those foolish notes called Valentines' was forbidden because it might remove the thoughts of the students from the underlying purpose of the school, the training of pious souls who were to go out and enlighten the world.

Yet Emily found the teachers kind and helpful. From the moment she set eyes on Miss Lyon, when the principal had come to greet Father and her in the school parlor, she knew she would respect and admire and perhaps love this leader of the faith, though she never accepted the doctrines themselves. How frightened she had been, sitting there in the parlor beside Father on one of the many cane-bottomed chairs that filled the room! Across from her stood a rusty stove, and at the left side a large cherry-wood table was pushed against the wall. It was really sumptuously furnished, she thought, but what would the teachers be like, how would they treat the girls?

And then Miss Lyon had come into the room, like a March zephyr with her capstrings flying, and wisps of red hair showing under the white cloth on both sides. Both hands stretched out toward Emily, who had risen apprehensively. 'You must be Emily Dickinson. Welcome to the Seminary family!' She clasped the hands of her new pupil warmly, and her startlingly blue eyes looked straight into Emily's, searching them honestly as she sought to discover the soul that breathed behind their depths. Would this one be a convert, or an impenitent, a delinquent? She might be either, but however she turned out, there was great capacity for thought in this young girl, Mary Lyon was sure of that.

Then Emily had presented her father, and Miss Lyon had invited him to stay for supper before his return to Amherst. They had taken their meal in the large, spare refectory at the principal's table, so that while it had been hard to say good-bye to Father finally, she had found the whole atmosphere much more pleasant and homelike than she had expected.

And now that she was used to the sea of faces all the time, there did not seem to be so many, and they soon became more than faces. They spelled new and warm friendships, and Emily found many here. The girls were quick to discover her talent for inventing strange or funny stories on the spot, and she was always in demand during recreation, or at the nightly gatherings in someone's room.

Not that she always went. The work was hard and abundant, and Emily wanted to make good marks. Her lively roommate left after the first week. Like many others who found the courses far too heavy and the social life too narrow for their tastes, she returned home to await marriage. Emily was assigned a new mate, her cousin, Emily Norcross from Monson, a plain, quiet girl, whose expression rarely changed from the flat, serious stare she had given Emily when she stood in the doorway the first night, a shoe brush in one hand and blacking in the other, and announced: 'I'm your cousin from Monson; Miss Lyon has assigned me to your room.'

Emily had seen her cousin a few times when she was little, but she had not remembered how colorless the girl was. It was like living with a sheep. But in a way she was glad, for the room was usually quiet, she could study as much as she wished. And there was a great deal of studying to be done in one's room, for the girls were well occupied all day long.

She sent a full account of their daily routine to the family one night during the third week of the term, sitting at the bare study table in the room after she had finished her Euclid for the next day. It was late, and she hurried the scratching of her quill before the retiring bell rang at eight-forty-five. She wanted to finish the letter, yet omit nothing, so those at home would know exactly how her days were spent.

'At six o'clock we all rise,' she wrote. 'We breakfast at seven. Our study hour begins at eight. At nine we meet in Seminary Hall for devotions. At 10:15 I recite a review of Ancient History in connection with which we read Goldsmith and Grimshaw. At eleven I recite a lesson on Pope's Essay on Man. At 12 I practice calisthenics, and at 12:15 I read until dinner which is at 12:30. After dinner, from 1:30 to 2, I sing in Seminary Hall. From 2:45 till 3:45 I practise upon the piano. At 3:45 I go to Sections, where we give all our accounts for the day; including absence, tardiness, communications, breaking silent study hours, receiving company in our rooms, and ten thousand other things which I will not take time or place to mention. At 4:30 we go into Seminary Hall, and receive advice from Miss Lyon in the form of a lecture. We have supper at six, and silent study hours from then until the retiring bell, which rings at 8:45 . . .' here the loud clang of the bell sounded in her ears, but Emily kept on, smiling at the words that appeared on the paper in front of her . . . 'but the tardy bell does not ring until 9:45, so that we don't often obey the first warning to retire. Unless we have a good and reasonable excuse for failure upon any of these items, that I have mentioned above, they are recorded and a *black mark* stands against our names. As you can imagine, we do not like very well to get "exceptions" as they are called scientifically here.'

She wanted to continue writing, to include comments on the various students and teachers, but that would have to wait for the next time. 'Done!' she said, weighting the quill in the glass of stones.

'And high time, too,' observed her cousin, who was already slipping her flannel nightdress over her head. 'You'd better hurry and snuff that candle, or we'll get an exception.' She pushed back her mouse-colored hair as she emerged. 'I don't care to have exceptions after my name.'

'You've taken the words from my pen.' Emily swung round on

74

the chair, eying the other impishly. 'Were you reading over my shoulder, Cousin Emily?'

'Why, of course not!' The toneless voice was shocked. 'How can you say such things! How could I see from here?'

'Never mind,' laughed Emily. 'All right, I'll undress at once. The room will be as black as this ink long before the tardy bell.' She corked the bottle, sealed her letter with wax, and straightened the study table before she prepared for bed.

When the tardy bell sounded some minutes later, two white forms were molded beneath the counterpanes on the twin cots which stood side by side near the window, the only light in the darkness.

'You see,' whispered Emily, 'there was plenty of time.'

'Yes, but only because I hustled you,' was the answer. 'Remember that I am a senior, Emily, and I wish to make a flawless record during my last year.'

'What shall you do when you leave here? Teach?' Emily wanted to know suddenly.

'I expect so. Unless' — here the older girl blushed in the darkness — 'I should receive an offer of marriage. Miss Lyon wishes us to become missionaries, you know. But I do not think I would care for the life.'

Emily raised up on one elbow, peering across to the other bed. 'Tell me, did you take long to decide? When did you accept the faith?'

'During my first term.' There was scarcely any hesitation. 'I accepted Miss Lyon's precepts almost at once.'

She would, thought Emily. 'But didn't you — well, didn't you hesitate or ponder it at all?'

'Not for long. God calls to us all. Where He leads we must follow.' This was a favorite remark of their teachers.

'But not leave the world behind us,' protested Emily. 'I'm sure He would not want us to miss the fun and the beauty of the world. Many things are of great value.'

'Only the Spirit counts, and the sooner you accept this fact, Emily, the better off you'll be.' Her cousin was sleepy and considered the subject at an end with this admonition she had heard so often from Miss Lyon.

'It counts, but not *only*. As much, perhaps, but not more,' murmured Emily to herself as she settled back. There was another answer somewhere, one that went farther, deeper down. But Emily couldn't find it. She would have to think long and earnestly before she could decide to become one of the school's 'penitents.' She began going over Miss Lyon's lecture of that evening, trying to discover whether she could agree with all the statements. But sleep overcame her, and presently her inaudible breathing mingled with the faint wheeze that came from the cot beside her.

While she was 'carrying the knives' for dinner the next day, Miss Whitman, the Assistant Principal, called to her. Emily's household task at school consisted of laying the knives at the tables and washing and polishing them afterward. It was a much lighter duty than she had expected when she came, and she did not mind at all getting the silver from the wooden rack in the large cabinet which filled one end of the long pantry, and carrying it to and from the twenty tables every day. All the girls had to help with the housework, and her share might have been much more tiring than this.

'You have a guest in the parlor.' Miss Whitman summoned her with a curt motion of her head. Her posture was straight and rigid as if there were a pole stuck down the back of her uniform. Her cap was tied tightly beneath her chin, not a sign of her gray hair showed anywhere.

'A guest?' Emily could not imagine who it might be. 'I wasn't expecting anyone.' She stood there with her hands full of table knives, looking at the Assistant Principal.

'Well, you have one all the same.' Miss Whitman grew impatient easily. 'Do put down those knives and follow me. Jerusha,' she said to the Abbott girl, who was taking down plates, 'will you relieve Emily?'

76

'Certainly.' Jerusha nodded to them. 'Do go along quickly, Emily, and let me know who it is.' A guest was an event with any of them.

Miss Whitman led the way down the hall and across the entryway to the parlor. When the visitor was a young man, as in this case, she herself saw to it that there was a chaperon. If she were too busy, then one of the younger teachers was called. At the sight of the fair-haired young man warming himself at the stove, Emily ran forward, happiness radiating from every inch.

'Austin, Austin! Did you drop straight from heaven?' She held both his hands, drinking in every feature of his face. He was a part of home come to the Seminary.

'I had to go on an errand for Father in South Hadley,' he explained, pleased that his sister was so delighted to see him, 'and I drove the horses their fastest all the way, so I could have more time to spend with you before I go back.'

'Isn't it lucky,' laughed Emily in sheer joy, 'that Father insists on the fastest horses in town? Oh!' she remembered the teacher standing near them, waiting. 'This is my brother Austin, Miss Whitman.'

The Assistant Principal relaxed and smiled. A relative in the immediate family was different! 'You do not look much alike,' she commented, turning from one to the other, 'and yet, now that I know, I can see the resemblance. Yes, your expression is very much the same. Will you not have dinner with us, Mr. Dickinson?'

'Do stay, Austin!' pleaded Emily, already leading him toward the dining-hall. But he did not need coaxing as he was quite eager to see what the school was like. He was attending Amherst College now, and the young men were always interested in hearing about a female seminary, there were so few of them. He knew he would be asked for a full report the next day.

The dining-hall fluttered when Emily entered with Austin, and before the meal was over, the whole school was charmed with him.

Those who were not close enough to converse with him were enchanted by his smile and good looks.

After dinner Emily escorted Austin through the building, accompanied by Miss Rebecca Fiske, a senior and assistant teacher she had liked immediately, whose plain face was ever alert and interested.

'My brother is a senior at Amherst,' she said to Austin. 'Samuel is his name.'

'Of course, Samuel Fiske — a fraternity brother of mine! I shall have to tell him I met you.'

So they were all friends at once, and Emily and Miss Fiske did not omit a single corner in their tour of the Seminary. After going through the classrooms, they took Austin through the long halls past the sleeping-rooms, which he later described as 'little white boxes of bedrooms,' and they stopped at every bay window for him to look out at the landscape.

'Just see the view from here, Austin,' Emily said time and again; and he exclaimed, 'Beautiful! Really beautiful,' with a smile for both Miss Fiske and her.

At last they returned to the parlor, and the young assistant left them alone. 'Now,' began Emily, placing two chairs side by side, 'tell me all about home. I know you're all well, but nothing else. How is Father coming with the railroad plans? How is Vinnie's pussy-cat? Has Mother been taking care of my plants?'

'Whoa, one at a time!' Austin put up his hand. 'Father seems to be coming along with the stock company. I think he's enlisted one or two more investors, but it's slow work, and there are times when he seems discouraged, Emily. He doesn't mention it, of course, just looks more solemn than ever behind his spectacles.' Here he pulled a long face like the Squire, and they both had to laugh in spite of themselves.

'Poor Father, I don't suppose he'll ever be able to express his feelings.' Emily's eyes suddenly grew thoughtful.

'And then the last few days he has worried about you,' Austin

78

went on. 'Emily Norcross wrote to her mother that you were having a cold, and of course the news was passed on to Amherst. I told the family I would see for myself how you were.' He looked her over anxiously. 'Your face is thin, Emily. Are you all right now?'

She was full of anger. 'Yes, I'm all right! It's true, I had a little cold last week, but our good cousin had no business to write home about it.' She took hold of Austin's arm. 'Please tell Mother and Father not to be concerned about my health. They'll make me come home if they think I'm not well, you know they will. And I don't want to leave, Austin!'

'I thought you were homesick.'

'I was,' she admitted, 'but only the first few days. I'm used to it here now, and I'd like to stay long enough to finish the first course, anyway. Long enough to — to find out something.' She finished a little weakly, hardly knowing herself what it was she wished to discover before leaving Mount Holyoke.

'Anything you say.' Her brother put a reassuring hand over hers. 'I'll take home a cheerful report. But don't work too hard, Emily. You'll only wear yourself out and have to come home anyhow.'

'I won't,' she promised. 'Now tell me the rest.'

So Austin supplied her with the news: Vinnie's cat had given birth to another litter of kittens, Mother had been tending the flowers in Emily's small conservatory every day (and complaining that they didn't 'do well' for her), Deacon Sweetser had a new horse, and Ben Newton had said last Sunday the house was like a morgue without Emily.

The last made her smile, and she asked him further about Ben. There were other questions until Austin thought she would never stop, but at last she had had her fill. He had told her everything he could think of and she was satisfied. 'Thank you, Austin.' She glowed with contentment. 'It was like having Amherst brought here to this parlor. Now that you've been here, none of this will seem strange any more. Part of it will be home because of your visit, even though you did come to spy!' she added with a twinkle.

He was forced to laugh. 'All right, suppose I did! But I enjoyed my mission, and I shall carry away a good report. I'd better be on my way, though, or Father will have to send someone to spy on me!'

They said good-bye gaily, each full of admiration and love for the other. Austin waved to her from the carriage as she stood at the front windows watching him. He pulled on the reins, cracked the whip smartly above the rumps of the Squire's steeds (there might be some heads peering from the upper windows), and was soon out of sight down the South Hadley road.

Emily turned and went up to her room, hugging his visit close. She wanted to go over all the news. It would be enough to keep her free of that aching nostalgia for weeks. But as soon as she came upstairs, the girls were upon her, Jerusha and Melissa and Jean Gridley, all those in her form, asking her about Austin.

He had been a great success, and Emily was glad, but she would have preferred being alone just now. The girls should have been studying, though they seemed to prefer talking, and sat around until the bell rang for lecture. What did Austin take most interest in? Who were his friends? Was he serious about any girl in Amherst? When would he be coming to Mount Holyoke again? These and a thousand more questions she had to answer concerning Austin.

Moreover, his popularity was not confined to the girls. The next evening she and Emily received a knock on their door during silent study hours. She turned the knob to find Miss Whitman and Miss Fiske had come to call. It was customary for the teachers to pay short visits to the girls occasionally.

'Good evening, Emily.' Miss Fiske's smile was always warm. 'Are you and your cousin comfortable?'

'Oh, yes! Please do come in, Miss Fiske, Miss Whitman.' This was the first time two instructors had come at once and the girls were quite overwhelmed. Emily Norcross scurried around setting

80

chairs out in the middle of the room, trying surreptitiously to pull a wrinkle from her bedspread on the way.

Both women made the usual inquiries: the girls' health, mental and physical; the study problems they might have; any needs they might feel. The routine to these little visits never varied. But after it was completed, the two teachers sat somewhat longer than usual. Miss Whitman appeared quite relaxed, her stiffness grown flexible, her prim expression almost pleasant.

'We certainly enjoyed your brother's stay here yesterday,' she said to Emily. 'He seems to be a fine, intelligent young man.'

'He certainly does!' seconded Rebecca Fiske emphatically. 'I liked the way he took such an interest in everything when we showed him around the building.'

'Thank you.' It gave Emily a feeling of happiness to hear them discuss her brother in such complimentary terms. 'Austin knows how to live better than almost anyone I can think of.'

The teachers stayed only a few minutes more. As they rose to leave, they offered the regular invitation, 'Now, you must come to visit us. Feel free to call at any time, girls.' And Miss Fiske added to Emily, 'Please come soon, won't you? I'm sure there is much we can talk about.'

'I'm sure of it, too,' Emily told her. 'I shall be glad to come.'

She had not yet been to call on any of her leaders, so she kept her promise and went to Miss Fiske's room one day shortly afterward. The young instructor lived at the end of a long corridor, in the same sort of room as the students', no larger, no more elegantly furnished. On the wall hung one or two framed certificates, and a gaunt book-case with its half-filled shelves added a forlorn air to the room. But the lively occupant made up for the lack of luxury.

'Emily, my dear!' She opened the door wide. 'This is a pleasure, indeed. Come in and sit down.'

'You see I took you at your word,' Emily smiled.

'But I meant you should! We will have a fine visit. I don't be-lieve anyone else will come today.'

Calls were limited to half an hour, so after a diverting thirty minutes of conversation, Emily stood up to leave.

'If you write to Amherst,' Miss Fiske said at the door, 'be sure to send my love.'

She didn't say to whom, but Emily chuckled as she went back to her room, 'It's not hard to guess.' Austin had come into their discourse several times again. That night in a letter to him, she added a postscript: 'Miss Fiske told me if I was writing to Amherst to send her love. Not specifying to whom, you may deal it out as your good sense and discretion prompt. Be a good boy and mind me!' This would leave no doubt in Austin's mind that his personality had captivated them all, teachers as well as students.

The days winged by one after another following Austin's 'mission,' and before Emily could realize it, Thanksgiving came. She had done well in her studies so far — Euclid was never hard for her, History she found most interesting, and her compositions in English here had the same welcome from the students as those in Miss Adams's class at Amherst. But she was still far from being a penitent, and Miss Lyon was beginning to look questioningly at her.

It was increasingly hard to decide, though she pondered the problem all the time she was not studying. Now she was going home for Thanksgiving. Home for four whole days, and she would not think about becoming a penitent till she returned to school; she wouldn't worry about repenting her sins, especially that of not belonging to the church. When you confessed to your sins, asking forgiveness through entrance in the church, you were a penitent. If you did not comply, you were an impenitent. It was left to the girls to make their own decisions in the matter, though Miss Lyon used her daily lecture as a means of persuasion. Some girls, like Emily Norcross, decided during their first 'series' or term at school; others, like Emily Dickinson, took a long time to make up their minds; a few went through the entire course without becoming penitents. Perhaps Emily would be one of them. She was disturbed, as she wrote a few weeks later to Abiah Root, her old friend: '*I am one of* the lingering *bad* ones, and so do I slink away, and pause and ponder, and ponder and pause, and do work without knowing why, not surely, for this brief world, and more sure it is not for heaven, and I ask what this message *means* that they ask for so very eagerly; *you* know of this depth and fullness, will you try to tell me about it?'

But now she pushed the whole question to the back of her mind. This was a holiday. She determined to spend the time enjoying her family and friends. She and Emily Norcross had their traveling-boxes on their beds, packing the clothes they wished to take with them. Emily had rebuked her cousin after Austin left for writing about her cold, and their relationship had been rather strained since then.

Now the other looked over at her. 'Emily . . .'

She looked up, her hand clasped about a shawl of wool lace. 'Yes?'

'The series is almost over, it ends right after we come back. Emily, have you thought any more about accepting the faith?' Her cousin's bland eyes stared at her without color.

'Of course I've thought of it.' In spite of the seriousness of the subject, Emily could not help being amused. 'I believe that's why we're here. But I cannot make up my mind,' she went on more quietly. 'I cannot see my way clear yet. Perhaps, later on I shall, but not just yet.' She folded the shawl and put it in.

Her cousin sighed and resumed her packing. She had definitely placed Emily among the sinners — there was no doubt of it and the Squire's elder daughter was touched by her concern. She walked around the bed. 'Don't worry, Cousin Emily,' she said earnestly. 'I shall get through it somehow.'

So they smiled and made peace with each other, and a few minutes later one of the girls announced that Austin was at the door. After Austin had tucked her in tightly with a fur robe, they drove off over the new-fallen November snow, with the sleighbells singing and the horses sending up little clouds of steam from their nostrils into the frosty air. Emily was silent most of the way, enjoying the drive and the prospect of the vacation before her. Her happiness grew as the familiar sights came into view one by one until at last the town itself appeared in the distance. Amherst had never looked so good to Emily as on that chilly November afternoon when she and Austin came driving in from South Hadley.

And as they approached the Mansion, she saw that the whole family was waiting to welcome her. They must have seen the cabriolet coming down the road and lined up on the front steps to meet her — Father, Mother, Vinnie, even the cat and her three little kittens! Emily flew up the walk toward them, and Austin drove the carriage around to the shed, smiling broadly to himself.

How good it was to be home! Emily went around touching things, she was so glad to see them — the marble-topped tables, the huge sideboard in the dining-room, her beloved plants, and the little mahogany desk in her room, beckoning to her like an old friend. She thought of the papers tucked away in its corners and was about to take them out when Hannah came up with a copper pitcher of hot water.

'Imly, dear, I know ye'll want to wash after your travel.' She bustled about, pouring the water into the flowered bowl on the washstand, laying out fresh towels and soap. 'Ye look too thin, studyin' too hard, I know!' Her shoe-button eyes still snapped, but there were lines around them in the rough skin, and deep lines at her thick mouth.

'Hannah is really getting old,' thought Emily. She had never noticed it before. 'I shall be fat from your Thanksgiving dinner when I go back!' she jollied, and Hannah was pleased.

'Go long wi' ye! Dinner will be ready now in a few minutes, so mind ye're not late.' She bustled out again.

Vinnie stuck her head in the door. 'May I come in? Oh, Emily, I've missed you so! Why don't you stay home now?'

'What, and lose out on higher learning? Vinnie, dear, as much as I love our home, I couldn't do it. Don't ask me why, but there's something I must satisfy — here.' One finger went up to her temple.

'Well, I'm glad you're with us for a few days, anyhow,' Vinnie dimpled. 'Now we shall have fun around here again!'

They went downstairs arm in arm.

❧

THANKSGIVING DINNER was all that Emily had predicted, from the turkey with chestnut dressing to the rich puddings and pies at the end, and afterward there was the question of accepting some of the invitations that had come pouring in since Emily's arrival.

'Well, we must attend Professor Tyler's tea, no matter where else we go,' decided Mother quietly but firmly. 'You remember, Edward, we weren't able to accept his last two invitations.'

'You are quite right, my dear,' nodded the Squire, 'but I believe we should go to Deacon Warner's as well.'

The three younger Dickinsons exchanged glances. They had other plans. Emily spoke up first. 'But we can't miss the taffy pull at Emily Fowler's,' she objected. 'Everyone from the Academy and College will be there. I can hardly wait to see them all, although I want to visit the Tylers, too,' she added honestly.

It was a problem. They finally decided on the Tylers for the family together, while later on in the evening, Austin could escort his two sisters to the Fowler residence.

The girls put on soft flowered dresses, and before Emily left she went to the conservatory for the sprig of jasmine blooming there. She was grateful to Mother for having taken such good care of it, as she loved to wear flowers no matter what the season, and unless they were coaxed they wouldn't bloom in winter. She placed the narrow blossoms in her hair deftly, with a feeling for their exotic quality. They looked white and bewitching in the red fluffs of curls that surrounded her face like a burnished halo.

'Emily, do you think flowers in the hair are quite proper?' The Squire raised his eyebrows when she came out.

'They're never proper, Father, only beautiful.'

It was one of those puzzling answers again, and he didn't make any reply, but opened the door for them. It was strange that he should have a daughter like Emily — he often felt uneasy about her.

The tea was crowded and pleasant. All the families they knew most intimately were present, and the warmth of friendliness filled the rooms and overflowed in conversation and village gossip, led on by the genial spirit of the hosts. Later, when dusk filled the windows, the young people slipped away and joined the group at Emily Fowler's, where the party was already in progress.

They were all in the kitchen, where a large kettle of syrup boiled over the open fireplace, and cries of welcome greeted Emily as Vinnie and Austin pushed her ahead of them into the room. 'Emily! Here's Emily Dickinson!' They all came running to her side, James Clark and Ned Twombley and Harold Holland, and Abiah and Jane and Elizabeth. Helen and Emily Fowler made her come and stir the taffy for luck.

She was brimming over with happiness at the fuss they made. Always surprised to know that people wanted and enjoyed her company like this, she felt perilously close to tears that rose in her throat. 'I think it's done!' she proclaimed, taking the spoon from the boiling liquid.

Two of the boys carried the kettle outside to cool, and the others followed to see that it was placed in the snow without being upset. Emily had a chance to catch her breath, and then she saw Ben Newton. He had been sitting on the window bench in one corner and came over to her now when she stood alone.

'Mr. Newton!' she exclaimed with pleasure. 'I didn't see you!'

'I don't wonder. I was waiting until you could,' he smiled. 'And it must be "Ben" from now on, Emily, or I shall have to call you Miss Dickinson. How would you like that?'

86

'Not at all, Ben.' She laughed up at him. He seemed taller and thinner than she remembered.

When the liquid was cooled by the snow and night air, and thickened, they each took a lump of it, pulled it out into long silken skeins till it became stiff enough to braid, and finally to cut into chunks. At first it was easy and then it became harder and harder to pull. With each tug it grew whiter and whiter, until, when it was done, there was a panful of gleaming white taffy for all to chew. Not that much of it was eaten; you made taffy for fun, but it was too much trouble to eat more than a piece or so.

They cleared away the mess and turned to playing games. At blindman's buff Emily eluded everyone successfully, climbing on chairs or tables if necessary to keep out of reach of the groping arms. No one was as fleet as she, but at last Arthur Peterson, a callow youth who called himself a great author and wrote long, dull columns on trivial subjects for *Forest Leaves*, chanced to touch the flowers in her hair and called out, 'Emily Dickinson, I've caught you!' pulling out the spray of blossoms and holding it up like a trophy.

She snatched it from him quickly, hardly knowing why, or what made her so angry, as if he had torn her dress or part of her flesh away. 'Why can't you be more careful?' she demanded. Then, composing herself hastily, though her hands trembled as she replaced the jasmine, she said, 'All right, blind my eyes.' She did not care to be 'It'; she was always confused and shaky when she couldn't see. But it was soon over, for Vinnie's giggle gave her away, and Emily pounced on her sister a few seconds afterward.

Lavinia took her turn then, and after her some of the others, until Austin noticed the time and said they must hurry. He had promised Father faithfully that the girls would be home before ten o'clock.

It seemed too soon to leave, but Emily didn't want to displease her parents on this short vacation. Nothing unpleasant must mar these few days. Ben Newton, who had not joined in the games, but merely sat watching the rest, now suggested that she walk home with him. She was very glad for a chance to talk to him again, and Austin took Vinnie along with some of the others.

The sky outside was scudded with snow clouds, only an occasional star pierced the gray blanket they formed. Emily and Ben walked slowly, both made thoughtful by the stillness of the night.

It was on this walk that Emily realized more deeply than ever before that she had a friend in Ben Newton, almost as if she had never known him till now. There was a change in his attitude toward her tonight; she no longer seemed a little girl to him. He made her feel truly grown up, and yet he still was her guide and teacher.

'You were angry with young Peterson tonight, weren't you?' he asked her.

'Yes — but it wasn't very kind of me.'

'Why were you so enraged?'

'I don't know.' She was puzzled. 'Only it was so indecent, so unfeeling of him! Flowers are such delicate beings . . .'

He smiled. 'You speak as if they had souls.'

'But they have! At least, I think they have, I'm not sure.' She passed a hand over her forehead. 'That's the trouble. I'm not sure about anything. The teachers at Holyoke are beginning to worry because I can't make up my mind . . .' She turned to him for help.

'Don't let them trouble you,' he advised her, 'or push you into any decision before you're ready. Remember what I told you about arriving at conclusions; convictions take a long time to form or they are worthless.'

'But the other girls seem to find it so simple! They're like sheep, going calmly wherever they are led.'

He gazed down at her through the misty evening. 'Some people are born wise, Emily, and it seems to me that you are one of the few. But it means that you must doubt before you accept, you can't help doing so.'

88

'The thing that bothers me the most is that I'm not willing to give up the earth for the kingdom of heaven.' A frown wrinkled her white forehead.

'Why should you? Perhaps heaven includes the earth.'

Emily stopped still and looked at him. 'Do you think —? But of course — that could be the answer, or a step toward finding it.' She realized that they were standing in front of the house. 'I suppose I must go in. I see Father waiting in the parlor.' She held out her hand. 'Thank you for pointing out a new path,' she whispered. And then suddenly she saw that the wind had blown aside the blanket across the sky and the stars shone through the ragged edges of the clouds. 'Look! It's written in the sky,' she said, and her shining eyes reflected the distant light.

CHAPTER NINE

S HE SAW BEN NEWTON again on Sunday when he came for tea,
and as she stood in the hall saying good-bye to him, he reminded her of their talk on Thanksgiving.

'Don't forget what I said about taking your time.' His mild eyes
were half-amused. 'Let no one rush you into immortality!'

But Emily was grave, for there was still a question she had not
asked him. 'And what about the salvation of my soul?' she asked.
'Miss Lyon says we shall be damned forever if we do not accept the
teachings.'

He shook his head. 'Religion is not a matter of professing one
creed or another. It's simply a question of one's own heart — a
way of living. We save ourselves, Emily, not by a repetition of
words or doctrines, but by the love and tolerance we show to our
fellowmen.'

It was as if a weight had been lifted from her. 'Yes, I see it now.
I won't let them scare me when I go back, thanks to you, Ben
Newton.' She gave him a smile so radiant he found it difficult to
step out into the night.

On the front portico he turned to look at his young friend again.
'And don't forget to dream!' he told her for the second time.

So he was still encouraging her, Emily thought as she returned
to the drawing-room. How was he so sure? What a deep understanding he had! Father, lost in the Bible, would have termed Ben's

words 'radical' and 'dangerous' if he had heard their conversation. But to Emily they were a lantern, a beckoning light. She made up her mind that if she ever revealed her secret to anyone it would be to Ben Newton.

The next morning Austin drove her back to Mount Holyoke, and before she could go up to unpack, a group of her classmates clustered around her — Jerusha and Melissa and Lovina and Jean Gridley.

'Give me your traveling-box, I'll help you,' offered Jerusha. 'Only you will have to pay for it!'

'Yes, you must promise to tell us a story tonight,' Melissa took it up. 'One of those wonderful, long tales of yours. We've been waiting here to make you promise. Do you realize there's no one like you in all the school?'

They surrounded her as she mounted the steps, and Emily was more overwhelmed here than she had been at the Fowlers', for there they were all her old friends, and she had only known these girls since school began. A warm feeling rushed over her, but she cried out gaily: 'You are all completely mad! There are at least two hundred and ninety-nine more like me!'

Nevertheless, she did tell them one of her most fantastic stories that night as they huddled in her room before bedtime, with one of them acting as sentry near the door to catch the sound of Miss Whitman's prim footsteps in the spaceway. They listened to Emily's thrilling tones with rapt attention, and she was grateful to them because they had not given her a chance to feel homesick.

Series examinations came, and she passed her tests in all four books of Euclid on December tenth, the day before her birthday. It was something to celebrate! Now she was going into more advanced study — chemistry, physiology, and the quarter course in algebra.

She studied long hours, eager for knowledge, for this academic education she was getting at last. And taking heed of Ben's words, she did not come to any decision regarding her status as a 'true

Christian.' In vain did her cousin search for signs that Emily was becoming 'tender,' in vain did Miss Lyon wait for the door to open and admit her auburn-haired pupil during the sessions of the impenitents in her private study. Emily was anxious to learn, but not yet ready to accept.

Moreover, Christmas was coming, and there would be another holiday. Perhaps she could have another long talk with Ben. She began to think of the presents she must give and of the happy celebration they always made of Christmas at home.

But on December twenty-third, the dread whisper spread through the school like a creeping flood: Christmas Day was not to be kept as a holiday! The girls would not go to their homes, but remain at the school in their rooms all day long, praying and fasting. It was Emily Norcross who first announced the news to Emily.

'Haven't you heard? Hasn't anyone told you yet?' she asked with a sort of triumph. 'Miss Lyon suggested it to us older girls several days ago. Doctor Beldon, the one who preached to us last week, you remember, gave her the idea.'

'But' — Emily was bewildered — 'Christmas is a day of rejoicing, I don't see why we should fast. I don't want to. Do you?'

'If Miss Lyon thinks it best — yes,' was the reply.

'Don't you ever think for yourself?' demanded Emily.

Her cousin opened her mouth to speak, and closed it again just as quickly. This other Emily was really frightening. She was so outspoken, there really was no hope for her.

'You think I am the black sheep of the Seminary family, don't you?' The Squire's forthrightness was in his daughter's voice. 'Well, perhaps I am. But to me honesty comes first of all.' She wanted to go on, to find some way of showing her unimaginative relative what it meant to doubt, and to ponder, and dream of dim concepts just beyond reach, of some wonder that was waiting for her to divulge, if she could only grasp it.

But it was no use. Emily Norcross sat over her books at the other study table with her mouse-brown hair in damp strings on the forehead of her mouse-brown face and stared across with her pale eyes full of pity. It would have been impossible to make her see. Emily Dickinson returned to the theme she was writing, but her thoughts kept straying to Christmas, and the more she thought about it, the more sure she became that she did not wish to spend the day closeted in this little white box, as Austin called it, with no one but Cousin Emily for company, praying and fasting.

Fasting! She thought of Hannah's good dinner, of the candy a friend had sent her last year. 'For once I have all the candy I want,' she had written in a letter. If she stayed at school there could be not so much as a single bite of candy or anything else. She sighed and resumed her work. There was a knock at the door, and before either of them could answer, Jerusha Abbott burst into the room.

'Emily, we have to report at Seminary Hall in five minutes.' Her braids bristled with foreboding. 'Miss Lyon has called a special meeting of the impenitents!'

'Oh, dear!' Emily put away her papers quickly, and brushed her copper curls and tied them in with a snood. She tucked a clean handkerchief in her belt and was ready. Jerusha held the door, and they went out into the hall, where they met others hurrying to the meeting.

'Do you want to fast?' whispered Emily as they went down the steps.

'N-no,' admitted Jerusha under her breath. 'But I suppose I'll have to.'

They reached the huge, bare room where most of the girls were already seated on the stiff rows of chairs, nearly seventy of them, waiting in silence for Miss Lyon to address them. She entered by the little door which led to her private study, and ascended the small wooden platform. She greeted them kindly, her clear, blue eyes full of solemn earnestness, her warm smile including them all.

'If I didn't like her so much,' thought Emily, 'it would be easier.'

Miss Lyon began with a long explanation of the meaning of

Christmas, impressing upon the girls the solemnity of the day, and ended with the announcement they all expected. It had been decided that the date would be marked by fasting if they all agreed to the plan. 'Now,' she finished confidently, 'will all the young ladies rise who are in agreement with this plan.'

There was a moment of hesitation on the part of Jerusha and one or two others, but at last, with a scraping and squeaking of chairs against the hardwood floor, they were all standing — all except Emily. She could not bring herself to move when her heart cried 'no' in answer to Miss Lyon's words. They were staring at her with open mouths, but let them! Miss Lyon looked so disappointed, as if she had been counting on this action to bring Emily into the fold finally, after so many weeks of training. The principal lifted her hand, and the girls resumed their seats.

Clearing her throat, Miss Lyon enlarged upon the program for Christmas. Surely this brilliant but wayward girl would appreciate a second chance. 'Once again, will all those rise who wish to spend the day in fasting and prayer.' Again every girl in the room rose, this time without a moment's hesitation, save Emily, who sat without moving a muscle.

A hush fell over the assembly hall, while the astonished girls gaped at their classmate.

'Please be seated, young ladies,' said Miss Lyon quietly after a long moment. She had no more to say on the subject. After a short prayer for their guidance, she dismissed the meeting without a word or glance in Emily's direction. Going into her study, she closed the door behind her.

Jerusha and four or five others from her form closed in around Emily at once. 'Emily! How could you do it?' 'Why didn't you rise with the rest of us? Miss Lyon expected you to! She was watching you all the time.' 'How queer!' They could not understand her action at all.

Emily looked round at them, half-enjoying the fact that they regarded her with awe for having resisted Miss Lyon's wishes. 'Yes,

I suppose it was queer,' she agreed, and her eyes twinkled. 'But I thought a lie would be queerer.' Still they stared. 'Don't you see, I couldn't go against my conscience. I had to do what seemed right to me!' She wanted them to realize the way it was, but she saw from their eyes that to them she appeared as an eccentric and daring revolutionary and probably always would. 'Excuse me,' she made her way out of the circle. 'I want to speak to Miss Lyon.'

The study was shadowy and very still. The Head sat at her desk without making a pretense at work, gazing out of the window across the wide, snow-covered lawn. She turned slowly as Emily entered. 'Come in, my dear.' She indicated a chair beside her with a grave nod. 'Sit down.'

Emily approached her and curtsied, but she did not take the chair. She spoke in a low, swift rush of words. 'Miss Lyon, may I go home for Christmas? I want so much to be with my family for the day.' She returned the older woman's long, steady look without wavering.

'I had hoped that you would be willing to forsake a visit to your home for the observation of the day as I had planned it,' Miss Lyon rebuked her gently.

Emily made no reply, and after waiting a moment, the Principal leaned toward her. 'Then you do not wish to spend the day with us in prayer and fasting?' The question hung suspended in air.

'No, Miss Lyon, I don't.'

The Preceptress leaned back in her chair and fell silent. The Dickinson girl had such a brain, she thought, such a way with words in composition. If there were only some means of bringing her soul into the kingdom of heaven! But her own Protestant beliefs would not permit her to coerce any girl to pray against her will. If this particular one wished so ardently to go home, she would be free to do so.

'Very well,' she decided at the end of what seemed an eternity to Emily, 'you may go.' A smile came into her eyes as she saw the face of her pupil light up.

'Oh, thank you, Miss Lyon!' Emily's deep curtsy had a suggestion of the dance, and in another moment she was out of the door and flying upstairs to her room for her traveling-box.

When the stagecoach came creaking over the snow, she was standing on the Seminary steps waiting, her cape fastened and her bonnet tied neatly under her chin, her mittened hands clutching the ribbons of the ungainly box. She climbed aboard, and the stage was a chariot of clouds on which she wafted airily away, as her classmates peeked enviously after her from behind the curtains of their little rooms.

The Squire and Mrs. Dickinson were panicky at Emily's recital when she reached home — such a rebellious spirit! But everyone was so happy to see her, and Austin rose in stout defense of her stand against Christmas as a fast day, that the matter was finally 'arranged.' 'I will write Miss Lyon a letter which you will take back with you,' her father said, 'telling Miss Lyon that we wished to have you with us.' And, he added to himself, what would Christmas have been like without Emily?

❧

THEN IT WAS OVER and she was back in school, studying diligently for midyear exams. She hoped to finish her course with high marks, though as to her becoming a Christian in the Seminary sense of the term, she had little hope or desire as the days went by. There was more to be taught in that sphere than they could teach her at Mount Holyoke, of that she felt quite sure. During Christmas she had spoken to Ben again and had found his ideas a fountain of fresh, amazing knowledge. What a pleasure it was to know someone like Ben! And she was only now beginning to talk intimately with him. Writing to Susan Gilbert, one of the girls she had known at the Academy, a few nights after her return, she said: 'I've found a beautiful new friend . . .' and then laughed to think how old an acquaintance her new friend was.

The days pushed on, and still Emily did not follow any of the little groups which nightly trooped into Miss Lyon's study when they were ready. Some of the girls were already leaving to teach as missionaries.

'Maria Greenwood is going to Iceland,' Emily Norcross told her one night as they slid under their cold sheets at bedtime.

'South Hadley is cold enough for me!' Emily's teeth chattered. She could not become interested in missionary work, though Miss Lyon urged the students daily to go out into the world and spread the gospel. 'Do what no one else is willing to do — go where no one else is willing to go'; this was the watchword of the Seminary. But Emily had no desire to go anywhere except in thought and soaring fancy.

'I shall explore my mind instead,' she murmured sleepily, 'and then I'll write a letter to the world.'

She went to lecture regularly with the rest, but she remained unswayed. She was absorbed with chemistry and physiology, and her section began reading compositions. They read once in a month, during which time they wrote two. Thinking about these left little time to concentrate on Miss Lyon's daily reiterations in regard to the soul.

One Saturday morning, she was looking over her account-book just before her turn to report at Miss Whitman's office. The girls each had a notebook in which they kept track of every penny they spent and what they spent it for, and once a week they reported the result to the Assistant Principal. Emily looked over her figures carefully. There were only a few items this week — a hairbrush, some ribbons, six envelopes from the postman, a bag of peppermints — and all were correctly recorded and reckoned. 'I'm learning to keep accounts in addition to other branches of education!' she thought with amusement.

Lovina came down the hall with the mail-bag. She enjoyed her work as distributor of letters. 'I think there's one in here for you, Emily' — she fished around in the pouch. 'Yes, here it is — from Amherst.'

The letter was from Father himself — usually he let Austin or Vinnie take care of the family correspondence — saying that he intended to send for Cousin Emily and her on the following Saturday to spend the Sabbath at home; Austin would come for them. He didn't say so, but Emily knew he must be lonesome for the sight of her. It had only been a few weeks since she was with them at Christmas, and already he 'intended to send for her.' Emily was glad, but she had to smile at her father's way of showing his affection. She would always have to read between the lines to catch a glimpse of it — indeed, he probably expected her to do so, as he expected them all to realize his feeling for them without the need of expression on his part.

In the next moment she wondered whether she would be granted permission to go home. It would be up to Miss Whitman, and what better time to ask her than now, during their interview? She gathered up her courage for the encounter as Jean Gridley emerged from the office after her session.

'Your turn, Emily. I hope your accounts are in order!'

'They are.' Then, in an undertone, 'Stiff as ever today?'

Jean glanced warily toward the door. 'Worse,' she whispered. 'I think she has a touch of rheumatism, besides!'

'How unfortunate!' Emily's tone was such a mixture of sympathy and satire, Jean had to giggle. The way Emily Dickinson said things! No wonder she was so popular.

Emily herself thought as she went in at the door that it could not have been more unfortunate, yet she was afraid she might not have a chance during the week to ask for permission, as Miss Whitman did not always have time for interviews. If Father's wish were to be carried out, she must make her request now.

'Good morning, Emily, I trust your accounts are in better shape than Jean Gridley's.' The Assistant Principal was crisp as a starched bonnet and full of business.

Emily presented her notebook, and Miss Whitman went over the figures minutely. 'Correct,' was her verdict. 'Your columns are quite neatly set down, and I am pleased to see so few expenditures. Thriftiness is one of the virtues many of the girls lack.'

'Thank you, Miss Whitman.' Emily gave her a winning smile. Then before her courage should ebb she laid Father's note on the desk. 'My father has sent a request that Emily Norcross and I come home for the week-end, Miss Whitman; he was going to have Austin come for us. May we go if my brother arrives Saturday?'

She was not prepared for the effect of her question, even though she had not expected an immediate grant. Miss Whitman stared at her, speechless. She could not say a word for some time, she appeared so stunned. Emily began to wonder if the good woman were having a stroke.

At length she shook herself a little, as if someone had jiggled the pole down her back, and asked icily, 'Didn't you know it was contrary to the rules of the Seminary to ask to be absent on the Sabbath?'

So that was the trouble. Emily hadn't the least idea it would be considered a sin to want to leave over Sunday. 'No, I didn't, Miss Whitman.'

'Well, it is right here in the rules and regulations.' The teacher took the Mount Holyoke Catalogue from a row of books on her table and flipped back the pages. 'Here,' she said, putting a finger in the back part as a bookmark, 'read this.' She handed it to Emily. 'Then you will know why I must refuse your petition.'

There was the law in full. Emily read it through, feeling the eyes of the Assistant Head bore into her with every word. 'I'm sorry, Miss Whitman,' she apologized. 'If I had known this, I wouldn't have asked permission to go.'

There was nothing more to be said; she didn't care to make an issue of the matter. Miss Lyon had been kind enough to allow her to go at Christmas, and Father would have to wait till exams were over, when they would have a few days' recess, before he 'sent' for her.

With the rest of the school, she spent the next two weeks in concentrated study, preparing for exams. The midyear tests were taken in one of the assembly rooms by all the girls at once, and the examination marks read off from the platform. Three hundred heads bent over the long white papers on the arms of their chairs, reading over the questions as they waited for Miss Whitman to give the signal to begin. Emily felt uncomfortable at the thought of writing down her answers with scores of scratching quills all around her. At the Academy exams had been given privately, as interviews between student and teacher in each subject.

She looked helplessly across the packed hall, wondering whether she would be able to concentrate here. 'It's so public,' she muttered to Jerusha, 'I feel naked!'

When it was over, the girls chattered and compared notes in the dining-hall. They speculated on who would pass and who fail; they wondered who would get the highest marks. 'A failure would be such a disgrace,' thought Emily fearfully as she listened to them. But she need not have worried, for her marks were all high and she passed in everything. It was a relief, and she started on her course for the third series.

The wind howled outside the Seminary and the snow blew in at the cracks of the windows, melting to a thin damp line of moisture each morning in the heat from the fire in the Franklin stove. An armload of wood was needed twice a day to keep the blaze going. The spaceways were chilly with drafts, and the girls were forced to attend four-o'clock lecture with capes and shawls about their shoulders to keep from freezing in Seminary Hall. Emily, always a victim of colds, fell prey to one she could not shake.

Her head felt like a balloon, her eyes stung, and finally a deep cough racked her day and night, hampering study and making sleep impossible. One morning, after she had been seized with fits of whooping all night long, her cousin said she really ought to take something. 'I have some hoarhound here' — she offered a bag of it — 'and I hope you will make use of it. Coughs are dangerous.'

100

Emily thanked her. 'But I'll take it as much for you as for myself. I'm afraid you are kept awake as much as I.'

'No, honestly, it isn't that . . .'

Emily laughed. 'I know better. Did I bother you very much last night? I'm so sorry. It isn't fair to make you suffer, too.' She was actually more concerned about keeping her roommate awake than worried over the effects of her cold on her frail strength. 'Perhaps I could tie something across my mouth, and you wouldn't hear.'

But nothing would help, the annoying cough continued, and a chance visitor from Amherst who had stopped in at the Seminary was shocked at the sight of Emily, so thin and pale, and trying to suppress a spasm every other word.

'Emily, dear, you must be very ill!' was her verdict. 'I have never seen you look so poorly.'

'Only a cold, everybody has them,' Emily told her lightly. 'As soon as I am well established in the new course, I shall rest more and it will go away.'

But the damage had been done, for her visitor returned to Amherst with a sorry tale of Emily's health, which she regaled to the Squire and Mrs. Dickinson over a cup of tea that very evening.

'I wouldn't be surprised, my dears, if your daughter went into consumption the way she's coughing.'

Mrs. Dickinson trembled at the mention of this dread disease, and Emily's father grew very pale. He was terrified, but he said nothing. Only when the tattler had left did he speak, and then it was with finality. 'Austin, you must go to fetch Emily this week-end and bring her home to us. She shall not ruin her health.'

When they told Emily her brother was in the parlor, she ran downstairs to greet him, but one look at his face told her he had not come to visit. 'What is it, Austin? You look as stern as a judge!'

'And you look white as a sheet!' he accused her. 'Hepsibah

101

Sommers told us how ill you were, and Father says I'm to bring you home at once.'

'That old busybody!' Emily was furious, though there was a pain across her chest from the persistent cough. 'Austin, I just have a little cold! You know I get them every year at the end of winter.'

'I have never seen you look as ill as this, Emily,' he said with a seriousness that was unusual for him. 'Do go up and pack your things. I've already given Miss Lyon a note from Father, and she has agreed to let you go with me.'

'Austin, I can't go now. The term has just started, and I'm doing so well, better than last. I want to finish the course!' She put a beseeching hand on his arm. 'Please take home a cheerful report the way you did last fall; remember?'

'That was different, Emily. You were not a ghost then.'

'A ghost — pooh! I've never been more solid and strong!' Her smarting eyes flashed, but the miserable cough betrayed her pretense, and she shook all over with the cold and hacking.

'Strong, indeed!' he said mockingly. 'Now go and get ready, or I shall have to show you my strength and carry you off bodily!' He smiled at her for the first time.

Seeing him soften, she tried to argue again, but Austin remained firm, and Miss Lyon came into the sitting-room to add her word. 'I'm afraid it is the only thing to do, Emily. You must get well, or you can never complete your studies. We shall miss you, of course, but before long you will be back with us as our most brilliant pupil.' She bestowed a fond look on her most promising student — even though she wished the girl had been more religious.

There was nothing more to be said, and Emily, blinded by tears, stumbled upstairs to pack. It was so humiliating to be called for like this! She hated to admit defeat in anything, and it was a blow to be forced to leave in the middle of her school course because of weakness. But somehow she managed to pack, between the tears and fits of coughing, with Emily Norcross helping her and trying to offer comfort in her stolid way.

'Shall you be back, Emily?'

'Yes — no — I don't know —' punctuated with deep barks from her chest.

'Well, anyhow, you would never be a penitent.' Consolingly.

Emily was obliged to smile in spite of her tears. 'So what would be the use of going on, is that it? What about chemistry, and rhetoric and composition? They're learning, too.'

'Oh, of course, only — well, you know what I mean.'

Emily nodded. 'And I'm afraid you are right, Cousin Emily. I probably wouldn't have become a penitent, or won't if I should return.' She wondered what caused her to feel she would not be back. 'But it was good of you to be concerned about me' — she put an arm about her cousin's sloping shoulders — 'and now good-bye.'

'Good-bye, Emily.' The flat, empty voice was as close as it had ever been to emotion.

In the downstairs hall, Emily's little group of intimates awaited her, for the news had traveled quickly, and by now the whole school knew that Austin had come to take her home. Jerusha, Jean, Melissa, and Lovina, even some of the others she hadn't known so well, were all there to say good-bye.

They sent her off with loving words, making her promise to come back as soon as she was well, and then Austin was helping her into the sleigh, making her as comfortable as possible with hot bricks at her feet and the fur robe, which he pulled up and tucked carefully around her shoulders. Once established in the familiar sleigh with its painted dashboard, Emily looked out over the fields of sparkling snow and decided to enjoy the ride at any rate. But as the horses went faster on the way toward home, and the icy blasts cut against their faces, she realized that she was burning up with fever.

Her mother put her to bed at once and called the doctor. The Squire had taken one look at Emily and shuddered with an inward fear that Mistress Sommers had been right. He got out the great bottle of spring tonic and set it on the sideboard for Emily to take when she was able to come downstairs. Mrs. Dickinson, Vinnie, and Hannah waited on her continuously, until Emily said she thought the cough ought to slink away in discouragement.

But it persisted, and visitors to the Dickinson home took away sad news of the Squire's elder daughter. 'Didn't I tell you?' Hepsibah was overheard saying triumphantly on the street. 'I knew she was ill!' 'Going into an early decline — that's the way with these frail ones,' was the opinion of Amherst's matrons when they discussed 'the Dickinson girl's case' as they stood gossiping in the common.

Emily resented their pitying attitude almost more than the evil-tasting medicine she had to take several times each day. 'I shall get well if only to spite their clucking tongues,' she vowed. And when a long month had passed, she was able to crawl from her room at last and to come downstairs for meals with the family once more. Her father insisted on a dose of tonic before every meal, and though Emily loathed it, she submitted to his prescription without a murmur, sensing his unspoken anxiety.

After another month of rest and treatment, the troublesome cough finally disappeared, and Emily was permitted to return to the Seminary for the last term.

'But it will be your last, Emily,' her father said gravely. 'I have decided that you are not going back next year.' His tone was definite, and this time Emily did not argue. She had found out what she desired to know about the teachings at Mount Holyoke, and her interest in finishing had waned. There were strange new precepts to be learned through the paths Ben Newton had shown her, and she meant to follow them.

The last term passed swiftly. She spent long hours outdoors, wandering among the spring flowers with her friends and dreaming of remote places in her imagination. She no longer worried over those nightly meetings in Miss Lyon's study which she could not bring herself to attend, and when the series ended, she found herself happy at the thought of returning home to stay.

The following fall she took courses at Amherst Academy once more, but this time only a few. 'You must not tire yourself again,' her father admonished her. And Mrs. Dickinson added, 'Besides, Emily, it is time you were learning to cook and bake.'

To her surprise, Emily found she was expert at both. She made a round rye and Indian loaf that took a prize at Cattle Show, and exceptionally good gingerbread.

She entered into the pleasant social life at Amherst, enjoying her studies at the Academy and the occasional gatherings which broke in on the daily routine of village life like little bells ringing merrily.

CHAPTER TEN

I T WAS GOOD to be back at the Academy. Leonard Humphrey was back, too, after his year at Andover, this time as a tutor in addition to his course, and Emily was overjoyed to see him. His eyes looked more hollow, his cheeks more gaunt, his mud-colored hair more stringy than ever; but his slow smile, full of hidden humor, remained the same.

'So the fledgling has flown home to us,' he said, meeting her the first day. 'Holyoke's loss is Amherst's gain.'

'Thank you, sir.' Emily returned his smile mischievously. 'Let me return the compliment. Perhaps you can teach me to fly, for I still haven't learned.'

'After a year at Mount Holyoke Female Seminary?' he demanded. 'Why not?'

She shook her head. 'I'm not sure. There's much learning to be had at Mount Holyoke, chemistry and Euclid and rhetoric, but not the knowledge I'm looking for.'

'I see,' he nodded. 'Literature courses are what you need. And we are going to have some clubs this year, a reading circle, and a Shakespeare club that I shall organize myself.'

A Shakespeare club! Emily's eyes glowed. She decided not to miss a single meeting.

The organization was soon formed, and its members met once a month at different homes. One young man acted as tutor and delivered a short lecture at the opening of the meeting, after which he called for discussion. The tutor varied from one month to the next, most of them queer, erudite scholars from Amherst, each with a different theory. Emily regarded them all with interest and amusement — you never knew what they were going to come out with next. But the afternoon the group met at Professor Hitchcock's she became very angry.

The young man who was presiding stood before them stiffly in his starched, ruffled shirt and immaculate frock-coated suit. He cleared his throat several times. 'It has been suggested that we use the Bowdlerized texts of Shakespeare in our study,' he boomed.

'Bowdlerized? What's that?' whispered Abby Woods to Emily.

The red-brown eyes shot sparks. 'Ladylike editions, with the most interesting passages cut out! I won't be a party to it!'

'Well, neither will I!' came from Emily Fowler on the other side.

'This will eliminate any embarrassment we may encounter,' the speaker went on. 'It will save the young ladies from blushing.'

'He's as stuffy as his shirt,' muttered Emily.

A vote was taken. George Gould, a tall, dark young man new at Amherst, collected the ballots; his mournful, rather brooding eyes lit up at the sight of Emily's angry ones, and a smile like sunlight emerging from a cloud crossed his olive face as he took the folded paper from her. He had an idea what her vote would be! Emily liked this new student.

Leonard Humphrey was teller. He counted the ballots carefully, and looked up bewildered. The girls in a body had voted 'No' to the suggestion. Most of the men had agreed to it.

The speaker cleared his throat again. 'What, may I ask, is the ladies' objection?'

Emily stood up. 'If we are to read Shakespeare, then let's read the lines, not cut them! Not one of them.'

Her statement started a lively debate in which Leonard, George, and Austin upheld the girls' stand for unexpurgated editions. Another vote was taken, and it was finally decided to let the plays remain as written for purposes of study.

Emily was still ruffled when the meeting broke up. 'The idea of anyone attempting to throw out one word of that master of words before whom we all ought to kneel!' She was standing with Leonard and George, who had come up to her.

Gould shook her hand. 'My congratulations,' he said admiringly. 'I'm glad you stuck to your guns.'

'Thank you.' She was pleased, but she was not calmed down completely yet. 'It's so stupid and irreverent,' she went on. 'A saint would lose patience!'

'I think one has,' laughed Leonard. 'Anyway, Emily, you made us think a good deal this afternoon, and that's what old Will wanted most, you know.'

This gave her some comfort. Austin joined them. 'It's nearly dinner time, Em,' he reminded her. Others came up, too, in twos and threes to say good-bye, so the discussion had to stop.

Just before they left, Emily Fowler took her aside. 'What about tomorrow night?' she whispered. 'Is it all right for us to come to your house?'

'As far as I know, yes. If anything happens to prevent it, I'll let you know. But it's all arranged, we've told everyone.'

'Good!'

'Come on, Emily!' called Austin.

And so the girls parted, full of thoughts of the next evening, when a very different sort of meeting would be held.

The moon rose round and rollicking that late autumn evening, and peeked mischievously in at the Mansion windows. Something unusual was going on in there!

Emily and Lavinia fluttered in and out of the parlor like pale moths in their sprigged muslin dresses, hovering over the room, giggling with excitement and whispering mysteriously. Austin ran his fingers up and down the piano keys several times, adjusted his

108

stiff white collar unceasingly, and now and again went to the front door to see if anyone was coming.

The Squire and Mrs. Dickinson were nowhere to be seen. They were, indeed, far away from the Mansion at that moment. They had gone to the funeral of a distant cousin and would be away overnight. Austin, Emily, and Vinnie were on their own, and it was the chance of a lifetime. Mother and Father had never been away at the same time before, and they might never be again. This was the night, therefore, to hold a P.O.M. meeting in their home.

P.O.M., Poetry of Motion, a dignified title for dancing, was the most daring of pastimes in Amherst. In spite of its high-sounding name, everyone knew what the Poetry of Motion club stood for, and its members were considered very wicked, indeed, by the strictest of Amherst's Puritan citizens. The club was the most popular one at the Academy, however, and its champions were upheld as brave, fearless souls by most of the students. The mere idea of a P.O.M. meeting in the Dickinson residence was enough to make the event a memorable one and would have sent Mrs. Dickinson to bed for a week with nervous prostration had she known of the plan.

Austin, from his post at the door, suddenly called, 'Here comes the first carriage!' And Emily and Vinnie hurried to join him in greeting their guests.

Emily Fowler, who had organized the P.O.M. club, and Susan Gilbert, in whom Austin lately took great interest, were the first to arrive.

'I never thought it would come to pass!' exclaimed Emily Fowler. 'A P.O.M. meeting at the Mansion. It's too good to be true!'

'Sh!' Austin put his finger over his lips. 'Don't even mention it to the walls. They might betray us!'

The girls tittered delightedly, while a shivery sensation of dealing with contraband tingled their spines. Susan took a large roll of music from under her arm.

'The Virginia reel and lancers are in there — and a waltz!' she added daringly.

'A waltz!' chorused the others. It was almost too much. The waltz was the latest dance. Only a few had been written in Europe, and little of the music had reached the United States. It was like Susan Gilbert, who had come from out of town to live with her aunt, so worldly and dashing, to have brought it. Emily smiled at her, but the others looked a little doubtful. A waltz, where the gentleman held the lady in his arms to dance, was really going too far.

'Who is going to play?' Susan went on to ask.

'We'll take turns,' decided Emily. 'Everyone wants to dance.'

Presently more guests arrived, Ben Newton, and Louisa and Fanny Norcross, the Dickinsons' cousins. They were followed by several carriagefuls in rapid succession. Everybody came at once, and soon the living-room was full of young people waiting for the dance to begin.

'I'm afraid we won't have enough room.' Emily Fowler, who considered herself the authority on dancing, eyed the available floor critically. 'Couldn't we take up that hearthrug?' She pointed to the lion's head resting in front of the fireplace, his body flat behind him, a huge brown fellow set off by a vague green background.

'Of course,' said Austin, and Emily and Vinnie helped him roll up the rug and shove it into a corner, far from the reach of tangling feet.

One of the girls sat down at the piano, a sheet of music before her, and the dance was ready to begin. They started off with a Virginia reel.

'All right, now, everyone line up, gentlemen on the right, ladies on the left.' Emily Fowler gave the directions and the reel began.

To be sure, the steps were a little awkward, the notes issuing from the piano sometimes quavered, but the spirit never faltered. They were dancing!

110

Right. Left. Cross. Sometimes somebody took the wrong direction and the confusion added to the merriment. Emily and Vinnie had not danced as often as the others, and their floundering attempts to keep up brought an extra flush to their cheeks. How exciting it was!

On and on went the music. Tireless were the feet of the dancers, every step, every new position a fresh delight. When the reel ended, they rested a few moments, breathless and happy. Another girl took her place at the piano, and the 'poetry of motion' resumed, this time it was lancers. The routine consisted of a set of quadrilles, more complicated than the Virginia reel, and requiring a good deal of instruction on the part of Susan Gilbert, who was more familiar with the steps than the rest, having spent much of her life in large cities. Susan had wisely let drop the subject of the waltz. She herself was not sure how it went, and she knew from the eyes of the Dickinson brother and sister that it would bring more embarrassment than pleasure to young people brought up in a village like Amherst.

As it was, the stately walls of the Mansion seemed to look upon the scene of revelry with astonishment, and Hannah, coming to the top of the stairs in her nightcap and dress to discover the cause of all the noise from below, was shocked into speechlessness. She hurried back to pray on bended knees at her bedside for the souls of the young sinners.

Lancers was followed by another reel, and this, being more familiar to all, became very lively. Laughter rang high and toes seemed to be feather-tipped. 'I shall float away in a moment!' Emily called to Ben Newton.

At ten o'clock Emily and Vinnie served some little iced cakes they had baked in the afternoon and tea from Mother's silver pot. When the refreshments were finished, the dancing was resumed, and it was after eleven before anyone was ready to stop. Social evenings in Amherst ended promptly at ten o'clock as a rule, and the neighbors who happened to be awake at that late hour looked

113

at the shining windows of the Mansion and wondered what could be going on. Lights in the parlor after ten! It was unheard of. The Squire was known for his strict rules.

At last the guests departed, with whispered consultations at the front door concerning the time and place of the next P.O.M. meeting. Everyone declared this evening to be the most successful the club had held so far, and Emily, Vinnie, and Austin received their honors with pride. Tired but happy, they closed the door on the last person. Then, as the hour was so late, they quickly blew out the lamps and went to bed.

Austin was up and out of the house as usual the next morning, but Emily and Vinnie slept late in order to make up for the night before. Unused to dancing, they had aching legs and backs when they finally arose, and it was a cold, tight-lipped Hannah who greeted them in the kitchen.

'The parlor wants some straightening,' she said icily. 'I'll not go near it.'

'We'll do it, we'll do it, Hannah! You won't mention the meeting to Mother and Father, will you, Hannah? — will you?' The girls looked so beseechingly at her that she finally consented to keep quiet, but she added warningly, 'Ye'd better hurry. Your parents will soon be home.'

Emily and Vinnie rushed to the living-room and began to set it to rights. The dishes were soon cleared away, the chairs put in their places, and a stray handkerchief or so picked up and put out of sight. Everything seemed restored to normal by the time the family cabriolet was to appear. Emily saw it coming down the road just as they were finished.

But Vinnie suddenly grabbed her arm. 'Emily,' she gasped, 'the rug, the hearthrug!'

Both girls dived into the corner and captured the lion. Frantically they stretched it out and threw it on the floor beneath the white mantel. It was hard to get the claws untangled, the thing went every which way, but at last it was down. The girls heaved

114

a sigh of relief and went to meet their mother. Father was going on to the office.

Mother greeted them with her usual quiet gentleness and removed the great black bonnet and cape she always wore at funerals. The girls asked her about their cousins, and she began to tell them the details of the funeral, turning in the direction of the living-room. Emily and Vinnie exchanged a quick smile as they thought how recently it had been righted. They felt sure nothing was amiss.

But as soon as she entered, Mother let out a little shriek: 'Why, girls, girls! What has happened? The lion's tail is upside down!'

Sure enough, the majestic tail was turned up where it should have turned down, and all the lion's members were topsy-turvy in all directions. Emily and Vinnie were at a loss to know how to explain the glaring mistake. At last Emily, who detested evasions, confessed, 'We held a P.O.M. meeting here last night, Mother.'

If she had said, 'There was a murder here last night,' her words could scarcely have created more havoc. With a cry of horror Mrs. Dickinson covered her face with her hands. A P.O.M. meeting, here, in the Squire's living-room! The shame of it, dancing like heathens.

'Girls, how could you do such a thing?' she asked brokenly. 'I don't know what will become of you!'

'But Mother, there's nothing wrong with dancing. It's splendid exercise.' Emily rubbed the calf of her leg somewhat ruefully.

'Emily!' silenced her mother. 'That will be enough. Oh, how can I break such dreadful news to your father? What will he say?'

'Wouldn't it be better not to mention it to Father?'

'Oh, Emily!' Poor Mother was too distressed to say more.

All day long she worried and fretted over the problem. But Emily and Vinnie finally convinced her that it would be best not to 'trouble Father with it.' In return they promised solemnly never to hold another P.O.M. meeting at the Mansion.

And they never did.

CHAPTER ELEVEN

I**T WAS HELEN** who organized the Unseen Trap. She had been away at boarding-school, but came back in time to enter the Academy for the second term, which started shortly after Christmas. She was already becoming worldly, as she had sworn to do, and when she appeared at the school in a long fur coat with a little toque to match set high on her blond curls, she caused quite a sensation.

'Everyone wears clothes like this in the city. Really it's nothing at all,' she said airily to the group of intimates who clustered around her.

'Doesn't it grow rather monotonous?' asked Emily with sly intent.

'Whatever do you mean? — Oh, Emily, of course everybody hasn't a fur coat. You know I always exaggerate!' Here Emily interrupted with such peals of amused laughter that her friend looked puzzled, but after a moment she went on good-naturedly, 'You're still a rogue, Emily. You should come to Miss Sears' for a year, I know you'd be a success. Your wit would really be appreciated there.'

'Don't you think it is here?' said Emily Fowler quickly.

And Sarah Humphrey added, 'After all, we're not exactly dullards in Amherst.'

'Of course you're not!' Helen hastened to agree. 'Oh, girls,

I suppose I'll always be tactless. Please forgive me!' She looked so disconcerted the girls forgot their hurt pride, and Helen at once began going over the curriculum with them to see how it could be livened up.

'She's like a crystal that sparkles and shimmers,' thought Emily. 'But beneath it all she has a warm heart. That's why you love her in spite of the glitter.'

They were all taking courses in literature and rhetoric, so it was natural that Helen should think of an essay club. 'Of course it must be secret,' she said, 'otherwise it won't be any fun. And the club must have a name. Let's see — how about the Unseen Trap?' she suggested dramatically.

They all agreed that it sounded very mysterious.

'But what is the significance of the title?' Emily wanted to know; 'it must mean something.'

'Mean something? Oh, I don't know.' Helen couldn't bother with trifles. But she was full of lightning inspiration. 'We'll ask some of the boys to join, and the idea will be to exchange subjects and papers with them. You'll never know what subject you may get, or whose paper you'll have to read. That's the trap!' she finished triumphantly.

So the club was formed, and it proved to be one of the most entertaining in the school. The UT's, its members, some twenty or more in number, called themselves. Fanny Montague, who was majoring in art, designed an emblem for them — a woodsman's trap of crossed branches over a pit with the letters UT beneath it. The girls embroidered twenty of these on small pieces of cloth to be worn at meetings only.

Like the other groups in Amherst, they met in different homes. Helen offered to have them first, since she had started the project. When the participants had all arrived, she handed them each a slip of paper on which was printed in Helen's bold, flourishing hand the subject or title for an essay. The young men were then asked to exchange subjects with the girls twice around the room, so that no one would know who was going to end up with his original piece of paper, yet they all had a general idea of the variety of subjects.

They were allowed half an hour to write. Then: 'Time's up!' called Helen, and they had to stop, perhaps in the middle of a sentence. 'Change papers!' she commanded, her blue green eyes alight with merriment. The papers, too, were traded twice around.

Then they were read aloud. Emily Fowler began with a little meditation entitled: 'The Spirit of God Is a Turtle Dove.' It was a lovely, delicate piece of writing very close to a prayer. 'Now,' she posed when she finished, 'who wrote it?'

'Mattie!' George Howland declared. 'No one but Mattie could have.'

'Yes, yes! It must have been Mattie, as it was really typical of her,' they agreed universally.

'Well, Mattie' — Helen turned to her when the quick decision had been reached — 'do you claim authorship or not?'

But Mattie, whom they so confidently expected would confess, since she was the most spiritual of the circle and always with a religious glow in her wide, gray eyes, shook her head slowly but emphatically. 'I would like to be the author, but I'm not.'

They did not contest the truth of her answer, but who could it be? Several guesses were ventured: Emily Dickinson? No, it was not her style. 'I'm much too wicked,' she murmured almost inaudibly. Helen — never. Abby Woods? — no. Mary Warner? — no. Nor Sarah Humphrey and Susan Gilbert.

'Well, it must have been one of you girls,' declared Ned Clark heatedly. 'Come, tell us which one!'

There was no reply; the girls all continued to shake their heads. At last a young cleric, whom none of them knew very well, addressed Ned with some embarrassment, 'Why are you so sure the writer is a young woman?'

'Well, I just thought it sounded like — then you're the one!' Ned exclaimed suddenly.

The other nodded, his face slightly red as the little company voiced its astonishment in no uncertain terms. But he took it in good humor. 'Now I know I have a feminine style!'

The next composition was read by Abby Woods. This, too, left no doubt in the mind of the listeners as to the sex of the writer. It was a treatise on new materials for pie and the fashions of the month. But this, too, was disclaimed by all the girls and turned out to be the work of none other than Ned Clark! His acknowledgment caused a loud uproar.

There were other surprises. Emily's essay on horses (her interest in Father's mares and the Deacon's bays had proved valuable) was mistaken for the work of her brother; while Austin's discourse on flowering shrubs was ascribed to her. Most of them didn't know that Austin also was passionately fond of all growing things.

Only a few of the pieces were attributed to their rightful creators, and as it was close to ten o'clock by the time they had gone around the entire group, the meeting was adjourned. But before they left, Emily observed, with a special smile for the new cleric: 'It seems to me we've proved that thought is not governed by sex. We write as individuals, not as male or female.'

The UT's met regularly twice a month, to develop as well as display their talents, of which they all had an extra share. They were the leaders of both Academy and College and took delight in vying with each other for supremacy, taunting each other with literary barbs.

Close to Saint Valentine's Day Helen suggested they have a party. 'Let's do something different,' she said. 'Have you any ideas, Em?'

'I'll have to give the matter serious thought,' mocked Emily. They were in Mary Warner's sitting-room, the three girls munching winter apples late in the afternoon. She took a last bite and set the core on a plate, already half-full. 'It might be good to get away from essays for once — and from our own attempts.'

'But isn't the Unseen Trap an essay club?' demurred Mary.

'Yes, certainly. But no matter how light we make of it, we're all pretty serious about our own work. I think Saint Valentine's Day should be celebrated by pure fun.'

'So do I,' Helen concurred with her.

'Since there are two of you, I suppose you're right,' said Mary. 'And here comes Emily Fowler.'

Emily had been helping her father, Professor Fowler, in his office after classes, so she was always late for the UT 'board meetings,' as the girls dubbed these little conferences. She came in now all out of breath, flinging an armload of copybooks down on the table. 'Sorry I'm so late,' she apologized. 'I do hope I won't marry a professor! They're always working overtime.' She pulled off her knitted gloves and began to warm her hands at the stove. 'Have you decided any business yet?'

'Only that we must have a valentine party — and a gay one!' Helen informed her. 'Emily says it must be all fun.'

'By all means,' assented the newcomer.

So the four of them settled down to some 'serious' planning. On the eve of Saint Valentine's Day, sometime after eight o'clock, everyone met. There were various games before refreshments were served, but the one which caused the most hilarity was one of misappropriated lines of poetry. Helen and Emily, at the latter's proposal, spent a good deal of time putting together lines from several different poets so that they seemed to make sense, but actually were utter nonsense. One of these read:

> Oh, woman in our hours of ease
> Uncertain, coy and hard to please,
> But seen too oft, familiar with her face,
> We first endure, then pity, then embrace.

Vinnie, who was not a member of the club, but whom Emily had invited to the party, was frankly bewildered. 'I've never read anything like *this* before,' she commented, to everyone's delight when the mixed poems were handed out.

'Nor will you again, I hope, Vin!' Emily explained the play to

120

them. 'Now it's up to you to discover the correct authors and poems.'

Wild guesses and argument followed, and a good deal of mirthful laughter. When those lines had been unscrambled at last, there was a demand for more. No one wanted the game to end. So another mismated stanza was produced, which brought about great discussion, for ten of them were positive the lines came from Wordsworth's *Ode on the Intimations of Immortality*, while the rest of them had various notions as to the authorship.

When they had finally come to an accord, settling on Wordsworth, Emily surprised them all by declaring: 'Wrong, all wrong! The lines belong to Coleridge!'

And with this the party came to a noisy finish.

❦

WHEN THE WARM WINDS began to blow over Amherst, Helen was seized with another one of her inspirations: 'Let's meet outdoors! Somewhere in the woods.'

So they found a grove of trees graced by two interlacing elms forming an entrance, a perfect gathering-place for the UT's on late spring afternoons. The spot became known as the UT Grove, and one day a sign appeared across the entrance: 'Procul, oh procul esti profani!' — 'Away, oh away — you are profane!' No one knew who put it there, any more than the notes which now and then hung from the trees, in Rosalind and Orlando fashion, addressed to some member of the club. The stillness of the little retreat was often broken by shouts of laughter caused by these sprightly riddles.

Essays continued to be written and read aloud. It was after Leonard had read a paper of Helen's that Emily pointed out at an impromptu meeting, 'Yours aren't really essays, Helen. They're narratives — and pretty tall tales at that!'

'They're not tall!' Helen defended her work. 'They're all stories based on real happenings, and stories interest me. Essays do

121

not.' She made a wry face. Then her expression suddenly changed and became animated. 'The things that happen to people, the gossip you hear on street corners, in the common, after church — that's what I enjoy writing about! If I were an author, I'd write novels.'

'Novels?' repeated Sarah Humphrey. 'Aren't they a little — well, risqué?'

'Pooh, no!' Helen tossed her head. 'The novel is the coming form. Perhaps some day when I'm really out in the world, I'll become a novelist — yes, I think I shall,' she decided with finality, clapping her hands together.

'If you do, you'll shine brilliantly,' predicted Emily.

'So would you, Em,' was Helen's quick reaction. 'Why don't you become a novelist, too? You're always interested in other people's lives.'

'Yes,' said Emily slowly, 'but for a different reason. I don't care about the outside story. I'm curious about what it does to a man's soul.'

'You're too deep for me,' bubbled Helen. 'Isn't it funny to think of the future? I wonder whether either of us will ever get down to serious writing!'

Emily did not bother to tell her vibrant, frivolous friend that she had already begun in her own unique way. Neither of them foresaw that Helen Fisk was to become 'H. H.,' the novelist whose books had a great vogue in the late eighteen-sixties and seventies, and are still good examples of that period of American fiction today; that as Helen Hunt Jackson, the name she took after her second marriage, she was to write her most famous novel, *Ramona*, with which she would one day zoom like a comet across the literary sky; while Emily Dickinson would be a luminous star, fixed and permanent.

CHAPTER TWELVE

I N BETWEEN MEETINGS, studies, and parties, Emily continued to have long talks with Ben Newton. He was a refuge in which she could always find comfort and help and a source of constant inspiration in her work.

For always the work went on, in brief moments snatched from hours of duty, during the Sunday rest, or occasionally at night when she could not sleep. Sometimes for weeks she would forget all about it, and then the urge came on her suddenly and she would fly to her little desk. Everything she saw, or read, or thought about became part of it, whether she recorded it or not, like pieces of an enormous puzzle she was slowly putting together without knowing what sort of picture she was striving to complete.

Ben brought her Emerson's *Essays* one day, and she looked at the title with something like awe. Emerson, the heretic, the revolutionary, or as they called him — the transcendentalist.

'If my candle would last, I would stay up the whole night through to read this,' she said. 'Will you explain what transcendentalism means, exactly?'

Ben looked into her serious young face, so full of light and shadow and inestimable depths, with tender amusement. 'You've set a great task before me, but I'll try. Transcendentalism means the belief that there is a quality which rises far above — transcends, that is — all that we know or see, and that man has the power to extend this quality even to the world of material things.'

'The world of material things! Yes, that's it!' Another piece to the puzzle, another answer to the question of life. 'Then that way' — she put a finger to the corner of her mouth, thinking it out — 'everything could be spiritual, and nothing, if it is good and beautiful, needs to be renounced.'

'Emily,' Ben predicted, 'I think some day you'll be a teacher, you're such an apt pupil.'

'Oh, no. I can only discover truths with the help of a tutor like you and then try to set them down. But I want them to be right — to have some value!'

'Perhaps if I could see what you've done so far,' he ventured. He had suggested this before, but always she had refused to show him anything.

Yet today it seemed to her the time had come. 'It will seem crude and unfinished to you, and I've only made a beginning, most of what I long to say is still in my head. And yet — if you would like to see —'

'When?' he demanded, interrupting her.

She laughed. 'What about Saturday? It's such beautiful spring weather, we might take a walk; and I might bring along a little scroll of foolscap I have upstairs.'

'Might, indeed. You must bring it; I won't be put off again!'

'All right, then, Saturday it shall be; I promise.' And she gave him her hand on it.

There were many things to be done between then, which was Tuesday, and the following Saturday. She had to write her column for the school paper, *Forest Leaves*. They wouldn't let her skip an issue since she had offered a contribution one day shortly after the memorable P.O.M. meeting.

'Oh, Emily, you're so funny! So droll!'

'Such a wit, Emily — how do you think of such things?'

'Your column is so much better than Arthur Peterson's. Don't give him a chance to bore us any longer; we want to read your column in every copy.'

They all coaxed her, and she consented to write a little piece every time. It was fun, playing with literary buffoonery, and it gave a carnival touch to the staid life of Amherst. Emily often laughed to herself as she slipped some gay nonsense into what appeared at first glance to be a perfectly sober discourse.

Thursday night Austin brought George Gould home for dinner. He was always bringing one or another of his classmates into the house, a welcome diversion for his sisters. Of them all, Emily found George the most to her liking, and Thursday he was in especially high spirits. He sat next to her in his threadbare coat. So many students at Amherst College were lean and poor, she reflected; it wasn't fair: studying so hard, they deserved the best! He attended her with mock gallantry, and once or twice she caught the Squire's eye upon them, as if he were trying to gauge the extent of the young man's interest in his elder daughter. She had to lift her napkin hastily to her lips to keep from laughing. Father needn't have worried, as she and George were only flirting. They enjoyed flirting with each other for the sake of pure fun.

Later she played the piano and Vinnie sang in a thin treble. No one in the family possessed any real musical ability, and their attempts were a source of amusement to all. George stayed until the last moment, nearly ten o'clock. It was such a pleasant, hospitable atmosphere, he didn't like to think of returning to his bare room in the boarding-house. Besides, the Squire's elder daughter was so enchanting; the way she threw up her hands suddenly when she laughed, the way her extraordinary eyes changed with every mood, the quick answer she gave to every quip he made! He admired her tremendously.

At last he made his reluctant farewells, and the family retired. Emily worked late preparing her assignments for the next day long after she was supposed to be asleep. Friday it was unusually warm for spring, and her head ached and her pulse throbbed from lack of sleep. She could not even attend the Shakespeare club meeting in the afternoon. She kept thinking, too, of her promise to Ben.

125

What if he laughed at her efforts? Or worse, what if he were kind and patronizing? She could not imagine Ben acting that way, but still a little scared feeling like a chill ran through her every time she thought of showing those papers she had kept hidden so long even to a trusted friend like Ben.

The sky was sullen that night. The clouds drew together in anger, hanging over the earth in threatening folds. Emily tossed on the great bed and vowed she would not go through with it. She would make some excuse to Ben. The sheaf of papers was pathetically thin, and the lines written upon them were terribly poor, she was sure of it! She turned again and pushed the counterpane down to the end of the bed; her head was sore with aching.

Then the thunder crashed and the rain fell, and somehow the spring shower brought release and she slept. Saturday morning dawned clear and sparkling as the raindrops that still clung here and there among the leaves. 'What a beautiful day for a walk!' thought Emily as she sat up. And all at once she was no longer afraid. If Ben thought she had no talent, then at least she would know. She would put aside the dream that drove her in an endless search for something she could not define, and she would settle down to being an ordinary citizen like everyone else. Perhaps that would be better anyhow.

Ben called for her at one o'clock; the law offices closed at noon, so the rest of the day was before them. Emily had tied her papers together with a crimson ribbon, and she swung the roll to and fro slowly as they walked.

'I'm afraid to show you these,' she told him. 'Last night I nearly decided to call off our walk.'

'There would have been no need of that, even if you had withheld your treasure.' Ben smiled down at the coppery head so close to his shoulder.

'Now you're laughing at me. But you're right, it is my treasure, and I hope you'll find some gold in it.'

'I'm sure I will.' He gave her his hand as they stepped onto a

126

narrow bridge which crossed the winding stream back of the meadow.

'But if it's all dross,' she continued, climbing the rough hump of boards with steps as light as a wood nymph, 'you have only yourself to blame, Ben Newton! Remember, you encouraged me.'

'I'm willing to chance it. I knew what I was doing.'

'Remember how you used to bring Vinnie and me books when we were still little things in short dresses?' she recalled to him as they went along. 'You always hid them in the syringa bush.'

'Yes. And one day your father came along just as I had slipped one under there. I bent down and began busily tying my shoe.'

They laughed. 'Father still feels the new books joggle your mind, and I suppose he always will,' said Emily. 'He simply refuses to discuss them.'

Ben nodded. 'I know.'

'Yet he has the vision to see the possibilities of the railroad, to spend his strength working for it, and he is beginning to talk about going to war on behalf of the slaves down South.'

'Those things involve action — they're tangible,' Ben pointed out. 'It's much more difficult to discover or accept new precepts of thought in the abstract. That's why I've always been so interested in you. You are a born truth-seeker. And now suppose you sit and rest here while I have a look at these,' he finished as they came to a large, flat rock. He took the roll from her before she could say no and untied the ribbon.

Emily sat very still, almost without breathing, her hands locked tightly together on her lap. There was no sound except the hum of insects, an occasional bird call, and the rustle of paper as Ben perused the pages. He read each word closely, a little frown of intentness creasing his brow. It seemed to her an endless interval that she sat there while the soft wind played about her face, and the damp ground grew spongy under the pressure of her small feet. But at last he raised his head.

127

'Well ——' she could scarcely bring herself to ask it — 'what do you think?'

He did not answer at once. He rolled and retied the papers, but remained holding them, his long fingers curled lightly around the roll, as if he were afraid of crushing its contents. 'I think' — he spoke slowly, measuring his words — 'that you have the power to become a great poet.'

He had said it — he had laid bare her secret with one word. It was as if a deep chord sounded in Emily's ears, a chime of bells that brought forth unearthly visions. Her head spun, and the color rose in her pale cheeks flooding her whole face and neck.

'I cannot believe it!' she stammered. 'Do you honestly feel that I could . . .'

'I know it, I'm positive of it,' Ben said firmly. 'There is an unusual quality in your verses that I have never found anywhere before. A certain direct forcefulness that is like the sharpness of steel, and yet the music is there, too.'

He returned the roll to her and took her free hand in his. 'You will have to work long and hard. The way will not be easy. But promise me you will devote your life's energies to developing your gift. Promise.' His eyes gazed into hers with an earnestness that went deeper than words. There was much more he wished to say, but he dared not. A sudden constriction in the muscles of his heart kept him silent.

But Emily saw none of the struggle and pain in her friend's face. Here in this old familiar woods he had unveiled an enchanting new country and bade her step within its realm. She was still beholding it, fascinated.

'I promise.' She wondered momentarily why Ben was so insistent, but her concern was lost in ecstasy. She thought she was going to faint with excitement.

IN THE MONTHS that followed, Ben was constantly her tutor and guide. He showed her the value of the lexicon, the value of pre-

128

cision in her choice of words, the fresh ideas in style or method that could be gleaned from one writer or another. All during that spring and summer he counseled her, until by fall she had formed the habit of calling on him whenever she hit a snag in her work.

Of course there were others who claimed her attention. She and George Gould kept up a lively exchange of books and wit, and often Leonard Humphrey joined them. Then there was Willie Howland who now and then came over from Springfield, and Ned Twombley, and oh, a host of others. She thought to herself with amusement that she was really becoming a belle! But it was always Ben to whom she turned for advice, whose friendly face was always there when she sought the answer to a tangled problem.

She did not resume her courses in the fall, so there was a little more time for writing, though the house was more often than not full of guests who came and stayed for weeks. She and Vinnie had to help with the extra work and cooking. It was a burden, but Emily managed to snare an hour or so occasionally, and she and Ben would talk over her progress.

They were in the library at the close of one of their 'sessions,' as they liked to call them, when he turned suddenly serious at her parting words, 'Next time I shall have more to show you.'

He looked out of the window without answering. It was February, and the snow was falling in swirls — thick, blinding gusts of it that obscured the countryside. Emily could never see a February snowstorm in later years without thinking of Ben Newton as he sat across the library desk from her that afternoon in 1850.

'I'm afraid we'll have to continue our sessions by post,' he said sadly, turning back to her at last.

'By post?' She didn't understand, she was troubled by his sorrowful eyes, large in his long, thin face. She tried to joke. 'If you mean you don't care to brave this fiendish winter weather I can't blame you . . .'

But he shook his head, smiling at her attempt. 'I'm going to leave Amherst this week, Emily.'

She caught her breath. 'You mean . . . forever?'

Again came the fleeting smile. 'I hope not! But my family has been in Worcester for three generations. I have decided it would be better to finish my law training there instead of in your father's office. By next fall I hope to be admitted to the bar.'

Ben — gone! It wasn't possible. He had been part of her life for so many years, she had never imagined a time might come when he wouldn't be there. 'I can't believe it!' she cried. 'What am I going to do without you?'

He was touched, but if he wished to say anything intimate to his young pupil, he did not permit himself the pleasure. 'My health is not all it should be,' he explained gently, 'and I think it will be better for me to live at home. You will have to work alone now — and perhaps that, too, is wiser.' He did not explain this, and Emily did not think of it until later. Now she felt only disappointment and a kind of helplessness. Ben recalled the promise she had made him in the woods and made her renew it solemnly.

A few minutes later he left, and Emily closed the heavy door after him slowly. She felt as if she were closing a book.

CHAPTER THIRTEEN

L IFE WAS INDEED EMPTY without Ben. Emily moped around the house for days after he left. She felt listless, without the desire to do anything. She realized too late how much his friendship had meant to her. All this time she had held a rare gem in her fingers without bothering to examine it, and now it had slipped through, lost, and she could only remember it.

'I know how you feel, Em' — Vinnie was sympathetic. 'It's too bad he had to go away!'

'I couldn't feel worse if Austin had left us.' Emily wiped her eyes. 'He said it would be better for his health if he lived at home. I never thought of him as strong, but ——'

'Father says Doctor Gridley marked him for consumption.'

'Poor Ben! So he was really ill.' Emily fell silent, musing again. If he had only told her, she would have tried to help him. She wouldn't have taken all he offered like a thoughtless child, without offering something in return. All she could do now was to keep her promise to him; she wondered whether she could work alone.

And then she remembered his saying it might be wiser if she did. Was there a deeper meaning in his words, was he thinking of himself as well as her? She would never know, it was only a matter of conjecture. But as for herself, she felt for Ben only a deep friendship, a love very much like the one she held for her brother.

Nevertheless, she missed him sorely. She couldn't get over the feeling that he was gone forever. Then a package came several days after his departure. When Emily saw the Worcester postmark, she hurried to her room where she could open it in privacy. She broke the cord and yanked off the paper in a second; there was a beautiful, leather-bound book!

'Emerson's *Poems*!' She held it lovingly, running a finger over the fine grain. 'How exactly like Ben! I can write to him now — let me see, in about two weeks — and thank him. Then he can answer my letter, and ——'

She felt almost light-hearted once more. Ben was still in the world, they could correspond and still exchange ideas. Perhaps he might even come back to Amherst on a visit.

She went downstairs and began to play *Maiden, Weep No More*, with such vim and vigor that Mother and Vinnie came running from the kitchen to see if it could possibly be Emily — who had hardly spoken a word to anyone all week. She smiled at them over the keyboard, and the look of relief that crossed both faces brought her a twinge of conscience. How careful her family was of her happiness and welfare!

That night at dinner Austin remarked, as he helped himself to another piece of gingerbread, 'The valentines are beginning to fly around school already, blizzards of them!'

'Foolish notes — stuff and nonsense,' grunted the Squire, testing the heat of his coffee with a silver teaspoon.

'More stuff than nonsense, Father,' observed Emily, with a special glance at Austin. 'Valentines are all we have to warm the blasts of winter.'

To this her father said nothing, his face retained its usual gravity, but inwardly he relaxed. Emily was her impudent self again. He, too, felt relieved.

'Do you have Susan Gilbert's address?' Austin asked Emily, casually, as if it had nothing to do with the valentines. Susan was away visiting at Geneva in upstate New York.

132

'So he wants to send one to Sue,' thought Emily. 'I'm glad.' 'Of course,' she said aloud. 'I write to her almost every week. I'll give it to you after dinner.' And I must compose a valentine or two of my own, she added to herself.

She hadn't realized how near the day was. Saint Valentine festivities were among Emily's favorites. That they were omitted at Mount Holyoke had been a keen disappointment, and she remembered how lonely she felt that year. Now she sat at her desk filled with gay mischief. First, she would pen some verses to Mr. Eldridge Bowdoin, partner in her father's law office.

To Mr. Bowdoin

Valentine Week (1850)

she headed the sheet before her. Then, easily and lightly, she composed a long series of couplets proclaiming the delights and privileges of Love. 'Done!' she declared gleefully as she folded and sealed the document. 'Bowdoin is becoming more of a bachelor every day. This will add a dash of spice to his dull fare.'

But the second valentine demanded more time. It was not rhymed, and was not in verse; but it contained more poetry, more wild imagery than the first. Emily let her fancy run riot in this 'letter' asking for an 'interview' with its recipient. Whimsy and humor skipped through the lines like pixies, yet now and then a philosophic flash gave body to the piece. When this, too, was finished, she took out a stick of her best sealing wax and held it over the candle, as the valentine was a very special one. She brought her little brass stamp down hard on the small pool of wax, and then addressed the missive to a student at Amherst College, putting on only his initials — two large, elaborately flourished G's!

Her eyes were bright with fun when she climbed into bed; she ardently wished she might be in George Gould's study when he received this gewgaw of wit and wisdom.

If she had been, she would have known delight and triumph, for

133

he was intrigued and bewildered by her delicious fabrication. As he read the racy lines, he felt greater admiration than ever for his unpredictable friend.

'Sir,' the letter began, 'I desire an interview; meet me at sunrise or sunset or the new moon — the place is immaterial. In gold, or in purple, or sackcloth — I look not upon the raiment. With sword or with pen or with plow — the weapons are less than the *wielder*. In coach, or in spirit or in body, they are all alike to me. With host or alone, in sunshine or storm, in heaven or earth, somehow or nohow — I propose, sire, to see you.' It went on in the same gay, half-mocking, half-serious tone for a page and a half. As editor of the college publication, *The Indicator*, he could retaliate in kind. 'This shall go into the paper at once!' he decided.

So into his *Editor's Corner* it went, with a note added by the editor himself. 'Now this,' he wrote at the conclusion of the valentine, 'is after all a very ingenious affair. If it is not true, it is at any rate philosophical.' He went on with remarks concerning the style and ability of the young author.

Austin brought the paper home, and Emily, reading the lines, felt the joke was complete. George knew how to play, there was no doubt of it, and so few people did!

But the sight of her own words in print gave her a queer sensation, almost of nakedness, and she resolved again to keep her work a secret. Publication did not interest her; she had put aside the notion of fame soon after she began to write, feeling it was childish and false, that acclaim was empty noise.

But she clipped out the *Editor's Corner* and put it among her keepsakes because of George. She saw him often in the next two months. She and George and Leonard Humphrey formed the habit of exchanging books and comparing notes on their readings. They went to lectures and meetings together or met at teas and 'levees.' Sometimes, if Leonard complained of being 'too tired,' she and George went alone.

Around the middle of April, these two were walking home from a lecture late one afternoon, when Emily exclaimed: 'Spring! There's nothing like it in all the world. I could live out-of-doors all during April and May!'

'Spoken like a true nomad!' laughed George. 'Only I'm afraid you would be rather damp in these showers,' he added as he helped her across a huge puddle in the road. 'May's the month — then it's heaven to be out.'

'Oh, yes!'

'Especially in an open carriage, driving like fury. Do you like to speed?'

'I dearly love it!' she vowed.

He was poor, he seldom had the money to hire a rig, and he had to spend most of his days studying if he wanted to graduate, but he said recklessly: 'Expect me suddenly. I am going to turn up and take you out for a drive some Sunday.'

And Emily experienced a thrill of pleasure at his promise.

May came along like an alluring damsel, wearing robes of filmiest golden green. The birds nearly burst their throats in song, and the skies turned the softest blue.

Vinnie decided to accept an invitation that had come from her cousins, the Norcrosses, the week before. 'I do so want to see Louisa and Fanny,' she said to Emily. 'Do you think you and Mother can manage without me?'

'Of course, Vinnie dear,' Emily smiled at her younger sister. 'You go and enjoy yourself.'

But she spoke without reckoning the ways of Fate, for the morning after Vinnie left, Mrs. Dickinson woke up with a severe attack of neuralgia that kept her in bed for several days.

It was up to Emily to run the household in Mother's place. Everything had to keep on with clock-like precision, and Hannah could not do it all. She was getting older in her ways and apt to overlook details in the housekeeping; it was usually Mother or Vinnie who tended to these. Now the burden fell on Emily, and she was frightened and helpless. Father and Austin were particular about meals; she had to see that they were just right, to say nothing of tending to a thousand and one needs for Mother.

Emily, who hated these duties like poison, must perform them all. Somehow the week dragged by, and by Sunday Mrs. Dickinson was feeling a little better. She still needed constant care, however, and it was with some misgiving that the Squire left for church with Austin.

'Take good care of your mother,' he cautioned Emily as he went down the steps.

She nodded and gazed over the countryside with longing. It was a day of rare perfection. She drew in a deep breath of perfumed air — there must be a million blossoms opening — oh, why couldn't she be out among them? But there was much to be done and she could hear Mrs. Dickinson calling feebly. She closed the door quickly.

At last her mother was comfortable and appeared to be almost asleep. Emily dropped into the nearest chair with a sigh. As she did so, the brass knocker sounded with a loud insistence several times, and she jumped up to answer the door before the rapping should awaken the light sleeper.

There stood George, hat in hand, his suit faultlessly pressed for once, his hair neatly brushed. He looked really handsome. Out at the hitching-post, a horse impatiently pawed the ground in front of Seth Nims's most shining surrey.

'M'lady, the carriage awaits.' George made a sweeping gesture toward it. 'You see, I've kept my word!'

'Oh, why did you have to pick today?' Emily felt like weeping. This was the last straw!

'But how could there be a better one?' He was hurt, mystified. 'Look at the sky and smell this air!'

'I have, and I would like nothing better than to go with you. But,' she explained almost in tears, 'Mother is ill with neuralgia. I can't possibly leave her.'

'Isn't there anyone else to care for her?'

'Vinnie is out of town.'

'But couldn't Hannah look after your mother?' His voice was tinged with exasperation.

'She is cooking dinner. Austin and Father will expect it to be ready when they come home, and Father would be very angry if he found I had run off.'

She looked so disappointed and despairing his dark eyes smouldered with angry indignation. 'It's a shame to keep you cooped up on a day like this. I won't tolerate it! You must come with me. Get your bonnet and shawl — hurry before the horse runs away by himself.' He was gay and compelling now, his smile came back in his eagerness to persuade her.

Emily was sorely tempted; she had never been driving with George and the opportunity might not come again, he was always so occupied with his studies. The balmy weather was so beguiling! For several moments she struggled against an overwhelming desire to run out and jump into the surrey before George could catch his breath; but in the end her conscience won out.

'I'm sorry, George. I can't go with you. I wish I could. Perhaps there will be another time.' She had made her decision and she was firm.

'Very well.' He took both her hands in his and brought them up under his chin, holding them tightly. 'I had something in particular to say to you, but perhaps it can wait till another time.' He turned and left her quickly.

What miserable ill luck that he should call for her today! Now that it was over, Emily shed angry tears in her bedroom. Mother was still sleeping, probably would be when the others came from church. Yet Emily knew that her answer would be the same if she had a second chance. Conscience would ever be the deciding force in her life.

By way of escape, she opened all the windows wide to let in as much of May as she could. Then she took a sheet of paper from the drawer and sat down at her desk. She was filled with dudgeon and disappointment at the same time, and only one thing could bring deliverance.

In a short while the words began to come, and then the lines. Her woes forgotten, Emily worked on, possessed of a feeling that was fire and ice. A vision swam before her eyes, and she strove to grasp and transfer it to paper ere it vanish. When she finished, her spirit, once more serene, was ready to float out of the window, a part of the spring day.

Dimly she heard Hannah calling. 'Em-i-ly! Your father and Austin are back. Will you set the table?'

Her feet carried her down the stair.

CHAPTER FOURTEEN

THEN IT WAS COMMENCEMENT, a still, white-hot day, full of expectancy. 'Everything is all in a buzz,' said Emily that morning. For when Commencement arrived, the town's excitement was at its height. Early in the morning the common began to fill up with fakirs' tents, peddlers' carts, and vendors of all sorts ready to sell their wares among the crowd. Workmen were arranging chairs on the stage at one end of the field where all the trustees of the College were to sit as they listened to the graduation exercises. By noon the whole place had the festive air of a county fair.

'Does my hat look all right?' Vinnie asked as she tried it on for the fifth time. All three of them — Mother, Emily, and Vinnie — had new bonnets which had come from Boston by stagecoach the afternoon before, and Vinnie could not let hers alone. 'Just see the ribbons, Em! Aren't they beauties?'

'Vin, I'm sure the graduates will be speechless after one look at you. They'll be so full of admiration they will forget their addresses — and perhaps it might be just as well!' chuckled Emily. She often wished these brilliant students were not quite so long-winded; some of them spoke for more than an hour without stopping.

Lavinia laughed too. 'But, Emily, we wouldn't want Austin's

shortened by a single word, would we?' she went on. 'Just think, Austin is an honor graduate.'

'Well, of course, what did you expect? And it's true, every word he says will be well worth listening to.' Emily had no doubt of Austin's ability. There would be another address to which she had no objection, but indeed a great interest. George Gould was graduating, and Emily was certain he would be a surprise to most of the dignitaries, Father included. Leonard Humphrey was taking his degree this year, too. No, this year she wouldn't mind the lengthy declamations which lasted more than six hours; but she didn't say so to Vinnie.

'Girls,' advised Mrs. Dickinson, putting her head in at the door, 'I think you had better begin to dress. You know we must be there before one o'clock. Father is anxious to see that everything is in order.'

'Tell him not to worry, we'll be ready on time,' Emily soothed her mother. She knew that the Squire, as one of the principal trustees, felt it his duty to see that the program went according to schedule; and today, because of Austin, he would be especially particular about the proceedings.

Vinnie hurried off to her room, and Emily took out her best spring muslin. If only it weren't so warm! She hunted up her little ivory fan even before she began to dress — she wanted to make sure of some small relief from the stifling heat.

Edward Dickinson awaited his ladies at the foot of the stairs. Without expressing the thought even to himself, he felt they were like three delicate flowers when they appeared arrayed in their best, though he did think Vinnie had pulled her neckline a trifle too low when she pinned her brooch. No time to adjust it now, though, and he marshaled them out of the house in his most dignified manner. He, too, was wearing new finery — a black, broadcloth suit that had come from Springfield — and he had ordered one for Austin as well. No occasion was quite so grand in Amherst as Commencement.

Dainty little Mrs. Dickinson's hand shook as she placed it on her husband's arm, and the girls were trembling with anticipation as they all went down the walk, climbed into the cabriolet, and started on their way to the common. They were among the first to arrive.

Father took his place on the stage among the other notables. There was the Governor of Massachusetts, sitting in state at the center of the platform, with prominent members of the faculty and clergy ranged on both sides of him. Missionaries were here from Syria and Burma and Hindustan. What stories they would tell afterwards at the 'collation' of strange foods, strange sights and peoples! Emily thought: 'I might have been one of them, coming home lean and sunburnt as a hungry native. As it is, I'm only a village lass and a sinful one at that.' She thought of her most recent escapade, running away after a funeral last week with Cousin Willie Dickinson, and driving home at a breakneck speed the 'long way around.' Father had not spoken to her for three days after that. 'But perhaps I have a different sort of mission in the world,' she concluded, 'one that will come later.'

'Emily — don't stand there dreaming!' It was Vinnie, who had found choice seats for the three of them. A row of empty chairs stretched beside theirs. 'Now watch for Emily Fowler and Helen Fisk and Sue,' she directed. 'You know we all want to sit together if we can.'

At last everyone arrived, the chairs were all filled, and President Hitchcock arose to present the honor graduates. The first one stepped up to the speaker's box and began his oration. His voice thundered out, and he spoke with flashing eyes and grand sweeping gestures so long and earnestly the sweat appeared on his forehead and rolled down his face in the warm sun. Emily waved her little fan incessantly and sighed with relief when he finished.

There were two more and then, 'William Austin Dickinson: *The Elements of Our National Literature*,' was announced. Father sat up straighter than he had been if it were possible and leaned slightly forward in his chair. Tears sprang to Mother's eyes, and Vinnie took hold of Emily's hand. 'Here he comes!'

Austin stood before them all, splendid in his faultless clothes and bearing, his fair hair softly waving, his blue eyes afire with young enthusiasm, and his voice rang out clear and strong. He had a well-prepared address, and his delivery never wavered.

Emily thrilled to every word with thorough family pride. Her eyes scarcely left his face, but once, when he was half through, something impelled her to turn towards Susan Gilbert, who sat next her. Sue's face was shining with a rapturous expression that could mean only one thing. 'So,' thought Emily, 'she returns his feeling. How wonderful! If I ever had another sister, I'd want it to be Sue.'

Next to the last on the program was George Gould, tallest and lankiest of graduates, whose oration was entitled: *The Relation of Self-Reverence to Christ*. He took the stage slowly, with great dignity, and a kind of expectant hush fell over the audience. He was truly a surprise, as Emily had predicted, and she felt a surge of pride in him, too, as if she had been responsible for his success. She had encouraged him all through his course; and now, his dark face aglow with spiritual emotion, he was proving her judgment. She realized that she was clinging to her ivory fan hard enough to crush it and loosened her hold hastily.

It was late afternoon when the exercises were over, and everyone was more than ready for the collation. This great supper, prepared by the professors' wives, was spread out picnic style on the College grounds next to the common. The ladies had fanned away the flies while the speeches were being made, and now they bustled about seeing that everyone was served. There were vegetables of all sorts, 'joints and tarts' topped off with watermelon and pies and cakes.

The crowd surged and overflowed the grounds, for no one in Amherst missed Commencement Day. From storekeepers to farmers and school-children, they all came. Youths and their sweethearts from neighboring villages took in the event, and strolled about the

142

common arm in arm, buying the souvenirs that the hawkers shouted for sale.

Emily loved the color and excitement of it, but, 'I wish there weren't quite so many people here today,' she thought as she pushed her way, along with Mother and Vinnie, to the speakers' platform. They showered Austin with praise, and though he waved them off deprecatingly, Emily knew he was gratified as his face was flushed with pleasure.

She saw George and Leonard for only a moment. She congratulated them both, and then, when one of the elders claimed Leonard's attention, she whispered to Gould, 'I was proud of you.'

His eyes burned into hers. 'That's all I wanted to hear. Now my work has not been in vain.'

Emily was disconcerted. She hadn't expected his reply to be so ardent. She stood toying with her fan, unable for once to make an immediate retort. Then they were surrounded again by people to shake hands with George, and several local swains to greet her.

She had supper with the girls who had been her old classmates at the Academy. Helen Fisk was truly becoming a worldly sort of person. She was away most of the time in New York and Washington, and only in Amherst on occasion. Emily Fowler was very interested in young Gordon Ford — perhaps they would marry one of these days.

George and Leonard Humphrey had to sit at the speakers' table, along with Austin and the other honor graduates. She was disappointed at not being able to enjoy more of their company, 'but,' she thought, 'I'll see them Wednesday, anyhow.'

For on Wednesday was the Dickinson Commencement tea. Throughout his career as trustee and chief patron of Amherst College, the Squire had given a tea between the hours of six and eight on the Wednesday of Commencement Week, and to the end of his life he continued the annual tea party for the graduates.

Mother, Vinnie, and Emily arose earlier than usual that morning. All the day before they had been polishing the silver, putting the

145

house in order, and now there were special dishes to be fixed and final touches made to the preparations. Hannah directed the hired man in setting up extra tables on the lawn and instructed her helpers concerning their duties for the great event. She gave commands like a general first to one, then another. Mother laid out the best silver spoons, the ones with little baskets of flowers carved on the handles. The tea service was all ready. On the sideboard in the dining-room was a glass decanter filled with sherry wine and a tray of delicate glasses.

'Emily, you will be here to pour for those who wish it,' decided Mrs. Dickinson as she arranged the gleaming ware a little more carefully. A rainbow flash of sun was caught and transformed into brilliant color each time she lifted one of the glasses.

'God's minor miracles,' thought Emily, 'are enough to convince the most thorough disbeliever. There's transcendentalism in a wineglass — a thought for Ben Newton.' Aloud she said, 'I think I had better pick the flowers now, Mother,' adding to herself, 'and deliver me from all confusion.'

Mrs. Dickinson nodded vaguely, already concerned with other matters. There was so much to look after, she was glad Emily always took charge of the flowers. No one else in the family could do it quite so well. Now where was that new tea cozy she meant to put over the hot-water pitcher? She went to search for it.

Emily meanwhile was in ecstasy. She held the scissors high in one hand and turned round and round the garden. What to pick first? They were all so beautiful and shining, it seemed a shame to pluck them. But she had a way of preserving them in water, a certain touch that kept life there long after the blossoms should have withered. She gathered armfuls once she had started and arranged them in bouquets throughout the rooms — roses, sweet peas, and honeysuckle sprays, lilies, and a low bowl of pansies for one corner. She was sorry the hyacinths were always through blooming so early in spring. She would have liked to put a bouquet of them on the mantel — oh, she loved arranging flowers!

146

At six o'clock the guests began to arrive. President Hitchcock came first with Mrs. Hitchcock. When Emily saw their carriage, she tied the sash on her sprigged muslin quickly and hurried down to her place. Mother and Father were still greeting the first-comers, so she flew to the little glass room and tucked the cape jasmines she had been saving for this occasion in at her belt. She was ready at last, and just in time.

The President was followed by the professors and their families — all the faculty were there at once.. They moved about the rooms, visiting with each other. Supper was handed around almost immediately: chicken salad and fresh-baked rolls, and then desserts, whips and charlotte russe, and many tiny frosted cakes. Most of the ladies chose coffee or tea, but the gentlemen came to Emily's corner to have their glasses filled and to chat with Emily. The Squire's elder daughter was charming, really delightful, if at times a trifle too 'advanced' in her ideas and manner.

For her part, though she enjoyed seeing her father's friends, several of them her former teachers, Emily wished they had not kept her quite so busy. She saw the different groups arriving, Susan and Helen and Emily, with a knot of girls they had known at the Academy; Louisa and Fanny Norcross, who had driven over from Pelham with Ned Twombley and James Clark, and who never missed their cousins' Commencement teas; and then the two she had been waiting for, Leonard Humphrey and George Gould.

They came in together, and paid their respects to the elders; how Emily longed to leave her post and run to meet them! As it was, she poured the wine with impatient hands, while the young men stood politely answering the questions put to them. George had been offered a year at a theological seminary, and those who had seen him through his course at Amherst wanted to hear all about it.

But as soon as the two could break away, they sought Emily out in the dining-room.

'We've brought one of Emerson's latest essays along,' Leonard told her. 'Why don't you come into the library with us? Hardly any people are in there. You can read it, and then we'll all discuss its merit.'

'Please do!' begged George. His dark eyes spoke another reason for wishing to carry her away from the crowd.

Emily busied herself with her task. She knew she could not leave just yet, Father would feel so mortified. 'I should like to,' she handed them each a glass of sherry, 'but you see, if I did, who would take care of guests like you that don't like tea? Let Emerson wait till afterward for Dickinson!'

Humphrey laughed, but George's eyes grew darker. Then they were both sucked back into the whirlpool of visitors who kept coming in great numbers and were received all over the house and grounds. It was a golden summer evening and everyone strolled about, laughing and conversing in little groups on the lawn as well as indoors. After a time, when there were not so many to be served, Emily slipped away to join Leonard and George.

When she entered the library, the latter was there alone, deep in her father's leather rocker. He stood up at once. 'I vowed not to leave till I had seen you,' he said.

'Leave? But why so early?'

'I must take the early train tomorrow to make final arrangements,' he explained. 'Union Seminary is particular about details, it seems.' He smiled at her.

'Tomorrow is too soon. Why must Amherst lose her scholars?' she asked mournfully.

He was delighted with her sorrowful expression. 'I'm glad to know my going grieves you so. And scholars can come back. In fact, it's quite a custom with them, isn't it?'

She nodded.

'I hope to return one of these days, and when I come, I hope you will be here.'

'And that no one in the family has neuralgia?' Emily cast him a mischievous smile.

148

Her face was so close, her red-brown eyes so alive and laughing, he could not resist. He bent and kissed her mouth.

Emily went scarlet as a poppy, and she heard her father calling, 'Emily! Judge Lord is here.'

'Don't forget, I shall be back,' whispered George as he left her.

She emerged from the library in a state of flurry. Judge Lord was one of her favorite people. As a rule she liked nothing better than to engage him in a battle of wits, but now she scarcely made any answer to his remarks, and the good judge thought Emily Dickinson looked slightly feverish. The crowd was probably too much for her.

Somehow the evening passed, and the guests began to make their farewells. She did not see George again, and she did not know when he had gone. If her father had not interrupted them, would the young man have made a 'declaration' then and there? Emily wondered. And did she want him to? It was hard to tell. She stepped into the garden and breathed in the soft, perfumed air. Austin was there, talking earnestly to Susan Gilbert.

CHAPTER FIFTEEN

W HEN THE SEPTEMBER SUN began to brown the cornstalks in the near-by fields, Austin boarded the stage en route to Boston. He was going to teach in a boys' school, an offer he had accepted before graduation.

With his departure, the household became suddenly quiet. The comings and goings ceased by more than half. The stir created by his preparations for one event or another was gone. The pleasure of his quick, knowing smile was sadly lacking. Emily would not go near his room, even to dust it.

'The walls are like empty arms,' she protested. 'Wait till he comes home on vacation, then I'll shine up every inch of the place!'

She missed George Gould a great deal, too, now that he was in New York at the Seminary. He had not written since he left. They had played a sprightly game together, and now it was over, or would there be a final round? He had said he was coming back; she wondered when.

Of course there were occasional beaux that came and went — Vinnie had her share of them, too — but the only one left who could match Emily's roving spirit was Leonard Humphrey, and she saw him rarely now that he was a full-time tutor. He seemed more preoccupied than ever, more removed from the world about him.

'My mother has written that I must come home for Thanksgiving,' he told her in November. 'But I hate to take the time; I'm working on a new outline for the literature course.' His eyes were sunken, his cheeks hollow.

'I think you should take a vacation, Leonard.' She was alarmed at the way he looked. 'At this rate, you won't have any energy left to teach the course after you've completed it!'

'The fire burns low,' he agreed, 'and I want to do all I can before the flame is put out.' His smile was whimsical, but his eyes were haunted.

'Don't speak of such things,' she murmured, frightened. She changed the subject abruptly. 'We enjoyed seeing you and Mary Warner the other evening, though the visit was all too short.'

'Yes, I was sorry she had to leave so soon. I could have stayed till dawn!' He pulled a book from under his arm. 'Here's *Pickwick Papers* I promised to bring. I know it will make you laugh. If George were only here, we should have some fun.'

'Yes — the wretch! He has not written to me. Have you heard from him?'

'Once or twice.' He gave her a penetrating look. 'George has an impetuous soul. He will swoop down on you one of these days.'

'Do you think so? I'll let you know when he arrives, though I may be decrepit with age!'

He laughed, and then suddenly began to cough. He controlled himself at once with great effort, as if there were something he wished to conceal somehow. They were standing in front of the library, and he turned from her quickly, consulting his watch. 'I have an appointment at four. Please forgive me, I shall be late.' He went into the building with the step of an old man.

Poor Leonard! Emily looked after him for some moments. They worked him too hard at the College. She would speak to Father about having Tutor Humphrey's hours shortened.

Even Father was tremendously busy these days; he scarcely took notice of what went on at home any more. In addition to the railroad, he was involved in politics, growing deeper and deeper, in

151

the question of slavery. It looked as if there were going to be some trouble; Negroes were escaping from the South every day and they told terrible stories. There was a special pew for Negroes in the church now.

Emily pondered the question of freedom as she walked home. She must write to Ben Newton on the subject in her next letter. Ben's health was poor, too; some months ago he had married a nurse twelve years older than himself. Emily thought his marriage would end their correspondence, but the letters had continued to come and they were a mainstay this fall. Each one brought praise and wise counsel, and always Ben urged her to go on with her work, never to let it lag for an instant.

Following his advice, she perused her lexicon with greater care, and spent more time in composing single phrases or lines. Words had a magic for her, and in the quiet of her own room she studied and played with them and juggled them around until she had formed a lace-like pattern of syllables and sounds.

Pigmy seraphs gone astray,
Velvet people from Vevay,
Belles from some lost summer day,
Bees' exclusive coterie.

What a wonderful sensation it was to write! In spite of her loneliness, she was happy at finding herself with longer periods for developing her gift, as Ben had called it.

She turned in at the gate with a resolve to devote an hour to her beloved writing that very afternoon, but Mrs. Dickinson met her at the door with a letter in her hand. 'Austin is coming home for Thanksgiving, Emily. We must get his room ready at once!'

So there was another delay, but such a pleasant one Emily could not regret it. Austin's brief holiday lit up the dull days since he had gone away like a sudden burst of sunshine in a leaden sky.

Then it was over, and the household settled down once more. She was in her little conservatory, pruning the leaves on the daphne odora plant the first day in December, when her father came in from the office. He stood watching her for several minutes without speaking. Then he said gently, 'Emily ——'

'Good afternoon, Father, I didn't hear you come in!' She noticed that his face was grave and shaken, and fear clutched at her heart like a cold hand. 'What is it, what is the matter, Father?'

'Emily, my dear, we heard a tragic report at the office this noon. Leonard Humphrey died last night.'

'Leonard — oh, no!' She held the scissors in midair, motionless. 'But I saw him just last week, the day before Thanksgiving.' It was unbelievable! 'He looked pale and weak, but ——'

'It was very sudden, a brain congestion,' the Squire told her. 'A great loss to the College. He was only twenty-seven.'

'I remember I was going to speak to you that night about shortening his schedule, and then you went to a meeting and we had to prepare for Austin ——' Her voice broke. 'How selfish people are!'

Her father touched her shoulder. 'I'm afraid it wouldn't have done any good, my dear. Leonard had this affliction all his life. Only no one thought the end would come so soon.'

'Please, Father, if you don't mind, I would like to be alone a little while.'

'Of course, Emily.' He regarded her steadily for some moments. 'You will be all right?' he asked anxiously.

She was already lost in that private world of hers he knew he could never enter, and he went into the library, closing the door behind him.

Emily stared at the pale sunlight that gave warmth and life to her plants through the glass windows. She felt stunned. She had been to many funerals (always unwillingly, for they were dreadfully cold, chilling affairs), but this was the first time death had come close to her. It must be a strange, incomprehensible force that could snatch youth away like that. She looked down and saw that she was still holding the scissors: it was the same as if she were sud-

153

denly to cut down the blossoming daphne odora! What unseen hand had been so ruthless? Who was the Reaper and how could you ever know? Mystery surrounded him like a shroud.

The months passed by, and life went on uneventfully in the Mansion. After Christmas the snow piled up in mounds against the house, shutting away those indoors more than ever.

On a Sunday evening after the cold had settled, Vinnie sat strumming at the piano, her high, thin treble quavering in some sad lament. The squeaky music was the only sound in the parlor, for Emily was reading and Mrs. Dickinson, wrapped in a heavy shawl and huddled in her chair, was trying to hem some towels, though her fingers felt stiff with chill. The Squire had gone out.

'Goodness, Vin!' Emily found herself unable to concentrate over the wail. 'You sound much grieved.'

'Well, it's a sad song, Em, just listen.' And she began to let her voice out in tones that were more teary than harmonic.

Emily listened to a few lines and offered, 'I suppose I ought to take to weeping. I'm pretty sure I shall, if you don't abate your singing!'

Vinnie paid no attention, if anything she increased the volume wickedly, and Emily, with a hopeless shake of her head, tried to pick up where she had left off. Mrs. Dickinson bent down and took off her slippers, rubbing the soles of her feet in an effort to warm them. 'Aren't your feet frozen, girls?' she asked, increasing the motion. 'Mine are just as cold as ice,' she assured them confidently.

Emily looked up again. 'Poor Mother. I'm afraid there's danger of icification or ossification, I don't know certainly which!'

Mrs. Dickinson squealed, 'Emily, you are a caution! Ossification, indeed.' Her laughter caused the pince-nez she wore for sewing to slip from her nose, and she adjusted it immediately, still shaking a little, but with her face straightened to hold on the glasses.

Emily watched her with a smile of amused solace. Her mother

154

never forgot to be a genteel lady, no matter what the circumstances. 'We can't allow our own mother to freeze to death,' she said. She went into the kitchen and returned presently with a hot brick wrapped round with flannel. 'I begged it from Hannah.' She placed it under Mrs. Dickinson's feet. 'You can have your bed-warmer now, she agrees, if I bring it back in time to heat it up before we retire.' She threw an afghan over her mother's knees and tucked it under the warmer. 'Now the icicles will melt.'

'Thank you, Emily dear. You can be such a comfort when you want to.' Mrs. Dickinson leaned back and sighed contentedly as the warmth from the brick began to tingle in her toes. 'I wonder what's keeping your father,' she went on. 'He was going to meeting, but no place else as far as I knew.'

'Here he comes now.' Emily's sharp ears had detected the sound of the approaching cutter before the others. It took a few minutes for the Squire to drive into the barn and bed down his horses. He came into the house stamping heavily and bolted the door securely for the night, though it was only a little after eight.

Emily went into the hall to meet him. 'Well, Father' — she took his high hat and cane and helped him remove his fur-collared overcoat — 'how did you enjoy meeting tonight?'

'It was scarcely enjoyable.' The Squire helped her hang his coat on the rack. 'The church being extremely cold, the most I can say is that it was uncomfortable.'

'And did it last so late in the cold?'

He shook his head. 'I stopped at Boltwood's on the way home.'

'I see. And how did you enjoy the tavern?'

'It was much more comfortable!' The Squire said, raising an eyebrow at her. He turned toward the parlor at the sound of Mrs. Dickinson's respectful, yet timidly commanding, 'Edward?'

'Yes, my dear,' Emily heard him say.

Although their words had been brief, the implication in their voices had been that of a joke. Her father had said all that was required when he told her the tavern was more 'comfortable.'

155

Most people couldn't see that the Squire's ironic dryness was his wit and laughter. Speech and noisy outburst were contrary to his nature, but this did not prevent him from indulging in a joke now and then. Emily chuckled to herself as she followed him.

After a few remarks concerning the weather and the supply of shavings for the stoves, he picked up the Bible, and was soon lost in his favorite reading. Mrs. Dickinson resumed her hemming, and Vinnie was still trying to master the ballad of the pathetic maid. Emily did not feel like picking up her book again — she would write to Austin instead. She described the family scene, the evening as it had been so far, in her inimitable fashion, and continued: 'Unless something new turns up, I cannot see anything to prevent a quiet season. Father takes care of the doors and Mother of the windows, and Vinnie and I are secure against all outward attack. If (ah, that "if") we can but get our hearts "under," I don't have much to fear — I've got all but three feelings down, if I can only keep them. I shall think of you tomorrow with four and twenty Irish boys all in a row. I miss you very much.' She put down her quill, seized by a sudden loneliness, and watched the snowflakes, white against the dark square of the window; whirling atoms of perfection each and every one of them. What a queer, mixed-up thing life was!

CHAPTER SIXTEEN

EVENTUALLY the winter was over, and Amherst blossomed into spring. Emily welcomed the new growth; it brought fresh life into the routine of daily tasks and fresh interest in her beloved garden.

'I think I shall change the borders this year, Vin,' she said speculatively. 'Let me see. Suppose we put the primroses along the south walk, and some of those pale blue iris would look well beside the columbine beds. What do you say?'

'Whatever you think, Em,' Vinnie acquiesced. 'But don't touch the hyacinths or narcissus. I want them where they are — all of them!'

Her older sister laughed. 'Vinnie, you will suffocate yourself among those hyacinths some day. Strong perfume must be used by the drop, you know.'

'I don't care, I love it, and the blossoms are so beautiful!' Vinnie pleaded.

'Don't worry, I'll not harm a single bulb! But how about the rest of it? Will you help me?'

'Of course. And here is Tom to dig some new beds for you.'

The hired man had come up as they spoke. 'Where you want them new beds, Im-ly?' he asked. His strong arms carried a sharp-edged spade; his short, stocky legs bulged muscularly through faded blue jeans.

Emily gazed up at him from the ground where she was kneeling. She pushed back her sunbonnet and stroked her forehead. 'I guess over there, Tom.' She pointed to a spot where she intended to try out some new plants. 'Turn the soil at least two feet deep.'

She gave directions with a practiced eye. The garden was her province, and although Vinnie often helped her, reveling in the heavy fragrances and showier flowers, it was Emily who took charge, whose floral harvest was talked of in all the village. Such heliotrope, and lemon verbena, and such magnificent day lilies! No one had as good luck as the Dickinson girl when it came to raising flowers.

They worked all through the morning in the soft air, unmindful of the passage of time until Mrs. Dickinson summoned them for the noonday meal. 'Goodness, girls, don't you ever think of the hour? Father will be here soon. You know he desires promptness at all times!'

'Come, Vinnie,' beckoned Emily in an undertone. 'We must away to grosser duties. Whoever invented the annoyance called housekeeping, anyway? I prefer pestilence!'

Vinnie's giggle filled the back hall as they hurried in and put away their garden trowels. She had to set the table that day, so she went ahead of Emily and was ready for work before Emily had removed her sunbonnet. She had the table set by the time Mr. Dickinson came to the side door.

'Timed like a clock,' commented Emily, now faultlessly immaculate herself. 'Father should have been a general, he's so insistent on punctuality.'

'Sh,' warned Vinnie. 'He'll freeze if he hears you talking like that.'

Emily did not care to endure a cold shoulder from anyone on such a wonderful day, so she closed her mouth and flashed Vinnie a knowing smile as their father came into the room.

'Good day, Father!' they chorused brightly.

Their father thought the tone was a little too gay. He could sense

158

incipient laughter in the air, but his daughters stood before him so demurely proper, he could say nothing; however, his eyebrows rose the customary half-inch, the signal that he was intrigued. 'Good day, Emily — Lavinia. I trust you have spent the morning in some profitable pursuit?'

'Not only profitable but pleasurable!' proclaimed Emily as they all seated themselves at the table. She launched into an enthusiastic description of the plan for the garden this year. Her eyes sparkled, and her auburn curls caught the rays of spring sunshine and turned them into fiery gold. As her love for flowers was a passion she could indulge with complete propriety, she did not have to hold her high spirits in check now.

The Squire listened with his usual sobriety, now and then offering a comment or suggestion. He was delighted when Emily became ardent about an interest he could share whole-heartedly, though his attitude remained unperturbedly staid and passive to all outward appearances.

Mrs. Dickinson had lived with her husband long enough to know the signs of pleasure in his countenance and she settled down to her food with silent contentment. She was glad the weather was warm again, the girls so happy today, and her husband so well satisfied. He had taken three helpings of beef! It was a peaceful, light-hearted meal, of which there were none too many (she didn't have to call attention to the reliable thermometer once!), and she was grateful.

By summer the garden was well along, promising fulfillment of Emily's carefully laid plans. She viewed it with satisfaction and had just brought in an armload of blossoms, the fruit of her labor, when Vinnie met her in the little back hall, better known now as the 'Northwest Passage' among the younger members of the family.

'Emily!' Vinnie's voice held ill-suppressed excitement. 'You have a caller in the library.'

'A caller?'

Vinnie nodded, her eyes dancing. 'George Gould has come

back!' The sisters had never discussed this particular youth's interest in Emily, but warm-hearted Vinnie knew it was returned and her announcement was a significant one.

'George!' Emily almost dropped the flowers. She remembered Leonard's words: 'George is an impetuous soul; he will swoop down on you some day!' Impetuous he was, to descend without warning this way. 'Here, Vin, put these in a bucket of water, I'll arrange them later.' She thrust the mass into Vinnie's arms, first singling out a rose to tuck in her bodice.

As she went toward the library, she could feel the color surging into her cheeks. He was standing in front of the fireplace, one elbow leaning against the mantel, tall and lanky as she remembered, with the same intriguing smile.

'George!' She held out both hands. 'This is the pleasantest surprise I've had in nearly a year!'

'Is it?' He did not let go, but kept her fingers tightly in his. 'Was the last time, then, here in this very room?'

Impetuous was hardly the word, he was a forward young man! She turned the color of the rose at her belt and made no answer. Instead she observed, 'You are looking very well indeed, George. May I ask what brings you to Amherst?'

'I had to go over to Northampton, so I decided to take advantage of being in the neighborhood and come to see you. I always keep my promises, you remember. And today I was especially fortunate. Look!' He nodded toward the window, and Emily, following his glance, saw the same surrey waiting outside the gate that had stood there on that memorable day in May. 'I trust your mother is not suffering from neuralgia this time,' he commented slyly.

Emily was forced to laugh. 'You really are remarkable! How did you manage to hire the same surrey?'

'I made Seth Nims rent it to me. He was ready to hitch it up for Emily and Gordon, but I convinced him they would be as well satisfied with another one, whereas I would not.' He looked at her

160

in sudden apprehension. 'You will go with me, won't you, Emily? We'll have a beautiful ride. Do say you'll go!'

'Very well,' she consented with a smile. 'Wait till I get my bonnet. I won't be a moment.'

Then they were on the open country road, riding through the summer afternoon with hearts as young and gay as the New England of their time permitted. George urged on the horses at Emily's request, and their laughter blew back on the air as they sped along.

'This must be the way Apollo feels, tearing across the sky,' cried Emily. 'Which planet shall we land on, sir?'

George laughed, and answered with some like nonsense of his own. What an utterly delightful creature she was!

But on the way home, he became suddenly serious, and when they were no more than a mile from the Mansion, he turned off into a side road. The boughs met over their heads in a cathedral arch, the birds darted out of the way of the carriage with startled calls, and the wild flowers gave forth a warm, pungent fragrance. At a particularly deserted spot, George pulled on the reins, and they came to a stop. It was very quiet, and somehow stifling; Emily found it difficult to breathe and then realized that she was waiting for George to speak.

He was still for several moments, his eyes on the loosely held reins in his hands. But at last he turned to her with determination. 'Emily, you must know my attentions to you have not been idle. When I — when I took the liberty I did last year at the tea, it was because I felt so deeply toward you. You must know that!'

She did know it, and she felt guilty, for she had really led him to it, without the same yearning that was his.

'But what I wish to learn is — if you care for me,' he continued, his dark eyes gazing earnestly into hers. 'Do you like me, Emily?'

'Very much, George,' she told him honestly. 'You are a charming companion.'

'That's not exactly what I mean; you see,' he explained, 'I am really asking if you care enough to be my lifelong companion. I am not a man of any means. In fact, as a minister just starting out, I shall probably have a struggle, but if you would be with me, helping me ——' he took her hand, and looked at her beseechingly.

Emily did not know how to answer him, she was covered with confusion. Somehow, she had never expected him to propose to her, though she should have realized from his darkly serious manner behind the mask of droll merrymaking that he was in love with her. As for herself, now that the moment had come, she discovered that she was not ready for it; her feeling for George was not at all what she would expect toward the man who was to be her husband.

Gently she withdrew her hand from his clasp. 'I'm sorry, George, but I cannot say yes.'

'But — why not?' He seemed shocked at her refusal. 'If you care for me at all, I'm sure we could be happy.'

She shook her head. 'The way I feel is not enough — it's hard to explain, but — well, if I ever marry, I shall expect to give my whole heart and soul, to be holding it out even as the man, whoever he is, asks for it. To me, marriage must mean complete union of the two who enter it — or else it is valueless, even wicked. Oh, you do understand, don't you, George?' She was sorry for the dejection she had brought upon him, but there was nothing else she could say.

He smiled sadly and took her hand again in both of his. 'You are a rare creature, Emily Dickinson. If Diogenes were here, his search would be ended! I'm disappointed, to say the least, to find that you don't consider your feeling for me great enough for marriage, but I think' — his eyes squinted speculatively as he tried to figure it out, to convince himself — 'I think I would rather lose you than to have your consent without your heart.'

She sighed with relief. 'I'm so glad, George, I knew you'd see! We had a good time together, it was easy to laugh together, but it would not be so easy to stand together during the storms. I, at any rate, would be a total loss!' She tried to resume the banter they

had always played so lightly with; but for once he had no retort, no gay or witty comment, and Emily was wise enough not to press it.

She fell silent, too, as George turned the horses around and started for home. During the drive she kept her eyes on the distant horizon, not wishing to indulge in idle conversation, nor give him a chance to ask her to reconsider.

He did not speak until they were in front of the gate, and then it was only to bid her a courteous good-bye after he had helped her down from the carriage.

'Good-bye, George,' she said fondly, giving him her hand. 'I want you to know I feel deeply honored by your proposal. I'm very sorry I couldn't accept. It's just that I can't go against my inner judgment.' She felt the old helplessness pour over her as always when she tried to explain; she remembered suddenly, for no reason, the day before Christmas at Mount Holyoke, when the girls had stared at her so blankly. What was the matter with people?

But George had made an effort, and now he tried again. 'I know. I know,' he repeated. 'Since you are the one in question, it's probably better this way. I'm grateful for having known you, Emily . . . and I shall always remember you.' With these words, he crushed her hand almost harshly; then, releasing it, he jumped into the surrey and drove rapidly in the direction of the livery stable.

Up in her own room, Emily thought over her most recent experience with mixed sensations. She had expected to be carried away on wings of ecstasy when the most vital question in life was put to her, and today she had known nothing but regret. The other girls in her intimate circle had been talking for some time now about the One who meant all to them; several were already married. Emily Fowler had found Gordon Ford. It was reported that Helen Fisk had become engaged to an Army officer, Lieutenant Hunt. Susan Gilbert and Austin were obviously serious.

Only she, it seemed, was immune to any all-consuming passion except for her work. Surely there must be someone some time who could claim her heart. It had not been her friend, Ben Newton; it was not George; she wondered whether she would ever fall truly in love.

CHAPTER SEVENTEEN

BELLS!' exclaimed Emily late one September afternoon in 1851. 'Bells at this hour! Whatever can they be ringing for? Vin, Mother! Come on, don't you hear the alarm? Hurry!' She cast aside the dustcloth, glad of the chance to put it down. She had been tidying the front parlor, stopping now and then to take in the beautiful, flaming sunset that flooded the western sky, a band of color shot out across the heavens from the golden ball; the Gentleman in the sky must have used all his palette on it. Now she would have a chance to view it from the outdoors as they went to the church to find out what the trouble was.

'Mrs. Dickinson came in, dusting the flour from her hands. 'These special announcements — what can be of such great importance just now?'

'The only way to find out is to go!' cried Emily, first out of the house.

'My apron is untied. Fix it, will you, Em?' Vinnie stood in front of her.

'We can't stop for trifles.' Emily went ahead, joining their neighbors.

All the village had run out at the sound of the loud ringing that filled the air; storekeepers came out of their shops, men came out of their offices, and whole families came streaming out of their

167

homes. Only a matter of rare importance, such as fire, could cause the bells to clamor for attention. It meant that all inhabitants of Amherst must gather together at once.

Mrs. Dickinson, Emily, and Vinnie went hurrying along with the rest, their quick little steps, like the other women's, almost a run, yet never actually so abandoned. Children and dogs tore past on both sides of them, and most of the men bunched together up ahead. Many women carried babies in their arms.

As the crowd moved along toward the church, murmurs of speculation rose on all sides — what was it? What was it? They came in a body toward the house of worship, and there on the porch stood Squire Dickinson, pulling the ropes with a forceful hand.

'I knew Father must be responsible for such a commotion!' exclaimed Emily. 'He is back of everything that goes on in Amherst!'

Mr. Dickinson held up his hand, and an expectant hush fell over the people; their faces were full of anticipation; the sexton wondered what piece of news Squire Dickinson could have to announce that he started ringing the bell himself, without a word of explanation. It must be truly important!

'Neighbors,' said Edward, after an appropriate pause, 'I wished everyone to come and enjoy the sunset.' And he pointed to the sky, soaked in gold and flame, and pale green and violet.

The villagers stared at one another, astonished. The Squire had called them all this way at such an inconvenient hour just to see a sunset? And Emily, who had been casting surreptitious glances at the western sky as they came down the road, could scarcely believe her ears; it was too good to be true!

Since the Squire had summoned them, everyone stood and watched till the last trace of color was gone. But what a strange notion to take into his head! It was plain to see where Emily Dickinson got her madcap tendencies; her father had some peculiar ideas himself at times, many of them thought.

But Emily didn't think so: she had made a discovery, added another piece to her puzzle. At last she had found out: beneath the

168

wall of reserve and unbending tradition which bound him, Father understood what beauty and the joy of life were — only, with the exception of an inspired moment like this, he was too *shy* to let you see! She drew a deep breath of contentment.

❧

FATHER was truly a remarkable person. In the next few months he worked tirelessly at forming the railroad company; there was hardly an evening that did not find him calling on some prospective stockholder.

Golden October passed in a parade of leaves, and with it the bright color of Cattle Show; winter set in before Thanksgiving, and this year the season seemed even quieter than last, with the head of the house absent so much of the time. Tender-hearted Mrs. Dickinson was worried about her husband.

'Edward, dear, I wish you wouldn't work so hard,' she said anxiously. 'The weather is so cold I'm afraid if you are out so much you may catch pneumonia.'

It was February, and a heavy snow lay on the ground. The Franklin stove in the dining-room threw a bright glow over the faces of the four of them as they sat finishing their coffee after dinner.

The Squire's cheeks seemed especially shining as he laid down his napkin at his wife's words, as if they were a cue or a signal for his own. 'You won't have to worry any longer' — he touched her hand. 'A great event will soon take place in Amherst.'

His ladies leaned forward with excitement while their coffee grew cold in the cups. 'Oh, Edward, what is it?' 'Hurry, Father, tell us the news!'

'Well ——' after his customary wait. 'The necessary subscriptions have been made at last. The Amherst and Belchertown Railroad is to go through.'

'Oh, Edward, how wonderful!' 'Father — the railroad — just think!'

'The railroad — after all these years! Father, you've done it.' This from Emily, with shining eyes.

Her father looked around at his admiring audience with immense satisfaction. He felt it a triumph to be able to tell them his work had not been in vain.

'Do tell us the details,' begged Emily.

'Sweetser and I signed the final stockholder this afternoon, bringing the amount up to the fifty thousand dollars we needed.' He felt expansive, now that he had started telling them. 'A ground-breaking celebration will take place next week — cannon shots are to be fired, speeches — I suppose I shall have to make a short one — all the rest of it — and we expect the road to be completed by June.'

'Shall we really be able to ride on it by June?' Vinnie was still incredulous.

'Of course, on the best passenger trains that can be had, and we're to get a fine locomotive from Taunton. You know there were three railroad charters granted last year, but the Amherst and Belchertown line is the only one that will go into effect at once.'

It all sounded so impressive, his wife and daughters fell silent in contemplation of this great honor that had come to their village through Father. Emily was thinking, too, of those who had been so scornful years ago, when Father had first set forth his plan. He had shown them all now!

'If Austin were only here,' Mr. Dickinson said suddenly, 'it would be complete.' He had missed his son more than any of them knew — Austin was always with the Squire in the village affairs — but this was the first time he had admitted his loneliness.

Emily sensed that it cost him a good deal to speak of it now; she rose from the table quickly, smiling at him. 'I owe Austin a letter; I'll write him the news at once!'

Upstairs at her desk she dashed off a note, relating Father's announcement. 'Nobody believes it yet,' she finished; 'it seems like a fairy tale, a most miraculous event in the lives of us all.'

The afternoon of the celebration, Emily and Vinnie accompanied Squire and Mrs. Dickinson to the common, where most of the town-

170

folk were already gathered. People stood around in groups, bundled up in greatcoats, shawls, hoods, mittens, and overshoes, breath rising in little funnels of vapor on the cold air from the busy mouths. News of the railroad caused a great stir, and men, women, and children talked of it all at once. What sport to watch the train come in! Think of the loaded cars! How often would they run? Through what towns? Sunderland, Montague, and Belchertown? A thousand voices babbled together.

At last, Deacon Warner lifted a silencing hand, and the crowd was still. He read a long paper announcing the construction of the new line, though everyone realized what he was going to say long before he spoke. Cheers and applause went up at the end, and cries came for a word from Squire Dickinson, to whom Warner had paid high tribute.

Emily was proud of her father's quiet speech, thanking those who had helped in the project, and predicting a happy future for the railroad. He made no reference to the disbelievers, showed no signs of crowing over the old-timers who had balked him.

Further hurrahs followed his words, and then, with impressive ceremony, the town cannon was fired three times. The people sighed with satisfaction. Emily looked at the faces around her. Next to her stood old Colonel Smith and his wife, who had been among the first to sneer at Father's idea. Now Mrs. Smith, with her arms folded complacently on her ample bosom, was saying to her husband: 'Well, I declare, we have got it after all!'

Emily nudged Vinnie. 'They've got it!' she whispered. 'Those good-for-nothings!'

'Sh!' Vinnie suppressed a laugh. 'She'll hear!'

'What of it?' Emily's eyes flashed. 'Yes, "we've got it," in spite of their pities and insults, and we'll keep it, too!' No one could attack Father without arousing her indignation.

CHAPTER EIGHTEEN

SOME THREE WEEKS LATER, Emily sat staring at the calendar on her desk. 'The ides of March,' she thought; 'something always happens to turn the tide of men's lives about the middle of March.' She wondered what could happen in this staid March when only the wind was playful and wild. Would it be good or bad? A little chill of anticipation went through her.

'Letter for you, Em.' It was Vinnie, who had brought the post. 'I think it's from Ben Newton.'

'From Ben? Oh, good!' Emily seized upon it eagerly. For some weeks she had not heard from him, and she had been waiting word anxiously concerning some lines she had sent him. Inside she found much praise, much insistence that she increase her output. The letter dwelt almost entirely on her, turning toward the end to the spiritual vein in which he had been writing more and more of late. His phrases had taken on the air of another world.

At the bottom of the page he said: 'If I live, I will go to Amherst; if I die, I certainly will.'

What could it mean? Only one answer came to her, vaguely, like the cold wind that slipped in through cracks so that you were but half-aware of its iciness. No, she put the thought away, quickly. Death had too much horror for her; she could not contemplate it without shuddering, especially since Leonard's passing. Perhaps Ben was really coming for a visit, and had added the last part of the sentence merely to show in what high esteem he held Amherst. Yes, that must be it, she told herself. But she still felt troubled and uneasy. She put on her warmest bonnet, buttoned her coat tightly under her chin, and started for a walk.

'Oh. Em-i-ly!' called Vinnie as she was closing the door. 'Take a look for pussy-cat while you're out, will you? I can't find him anywhere. I just know he's strayed away this time!'

Dear Vinnie; her greatest concern next to her family was the cat of the moment; if one did 'stray away' or come to some ill-fated end, she always managed to find another. Emily's feelings were certainly not conducive to cat-hunting, but she forced a cheery answer. 'Stop chafing, I'll keep one eye open for him! He'll probably turn up before I get back, anyhow.'

The March blasts blew across the fields with such force, she could hardly push against them, but she kept on, impelled by some inner urge to battle the elements as a means of conquering her fear for Ben Newton. For more than an hour she walked, or strove to walk, in the teeth of a mean, complaining, moaning wind; and then, exhausted, she turned around and let it push her home.

She came in with the mood still heavy upon her; she couldn't shake it. Vinnie, too, was somber — her kitten had not shown himself, and she had resigned herself to his demise. Neither of the girls could eat much supper, and their father looked annoyed and anxious.

'Come, come, this will never do. If this keeps on, you must both take spring tonic.' He set the bowl of baked beans down with a firm hand.

This was enough of a threat for his daughters. They managed to finish the food on their plates, although silently and with inward avowals never to force their children to eat — should they ever have any. 'Indeed,' thought Emily, 'Father does not seem to real-ize that we haven't been children for many years now. I suppose he never will!' And she smiled indulgently.

For that matter, she did not feel grown up in several respects, though she was in her twenty-third year, and she had a strong suspicion the sheltered life under Father's roof was responsible. In some ways she was much older than the girls of her age and in some ways so much younger. The shadow of insecurity and uneasiness that had fallen upon her this afternoon frightened her and made her feel utterly helpless and inexperienced. She lacked any inner fortitude to take hold of and give her strength at times like these.

When they had gone into the drawing-room and settled themselves to reading and sewing till bedtime, Father asked her to play for him, and she seated herself at the piano, though she had no desire for some of the ballads he wished to hear. Unconsciously she began to beat out the stirring passages of *The Erlking*, music as wild and mournful as the wind outdoors.

'What's that, child?' Mr. Dickinson started at the sound.

'*The Erlking*, Father, death riding away with the little boy, you remember.'

'Pray, give us something more cheerful. We do not care to listen to anything morbid,' he bade her.

So she played a few light waltzes and a little gavotte, though she was not much inclined to do so. But after a while she stopped even these. 'I'm sorry, Father, my mind is out of tune tonight.'

'Very well, Emily.' He resumed his reading, and Emily took up her needlework.

The room was so quiet that the faint mew which came from the front steps a short time later was easily heard. Vinnie jumped up joyously and ran to let its owner make a bedraggled entrance, his coat matted and altogether the worse for his wandering.

His mistress hurried to satisfy his wants with some warm milk and meat, her good humor and happiness restored. 'Just listen to him purr, Emily! He loves to be fed and stroked at once.' Vinnie petted his soft fur as he drank the milk from the saucer on the kitchen floor.

174

Emily stood against the cabinet watching, but she made no move to shower the cat with caresses, for this was one delight she could never share with Vinnie. 'You'll make a plutocrat of him, Vin!' She was glad her younger sister had become sunshiny again.

As for herself, though she teased and taunted playfully, she couldn't shake the feeling of disaster that had crept into her very bones and refused to be pushed aside. She stayed awake a long restless hour that night before sleep came to her.

In the morning, her heart was still heavy, even the thrill of seeing her loaves come out especially crisp and brown was missing, somehow. But as the day wore on, and some of the neighbors dropped in for a friendly call, the nameless fear slowly lessened and a sprightliness came back to her speech. By the following day, she had almost forgotten the shadow. She answered Ben's letter in a purposely carefree tone, hoping his reply would chase away the last of her dark augury.

Two weeks afterward she had received no answer, but this did not seem unusual, since Ben often took more than a month to write. She came in from her garden, where she had been prodding the earth around the tulip tips that were just showing through, and noticed that the latest copy of the *Springfield Republican* lay unopened on the table. It was always a treat to read a new issue before anyone else had seen it. She washed her mud-caked hands quickly, and sat down in Father's chair, opening the paper. 'I'll be King for an hour,' she chirped, 'till Father comes home!'

But as she turned the page, her eye fell upon three shocking lines; the smile vanished, turning into a look of agony; and her body became a lump of stone, she could not move it. There, in those three, horrible sentences, was the blackness she had felt in the distance two weeks before. It was an announcement of the death of Benjamin Franklin Newton, of Worcester.

He had gone out quietly, at the age of only thirty-two, a victim of tuberculosis. The words said he had been ill for many months.

Emily could not move. She tried, but she couldn't get out of the chair. It was more than an hour till the Squire found her when he came in for his customary rest with his paper.

'Well, Emily, have you usurped ——' he began, but stopped when he saw her face. 'Emily, daughter, what is it?' His own skin went deadly white.

She tried to answer, but could not. At last she pointed to the brief notice. 'Ben — see, Ben Newton.'

Her father glanced at the announcement with alarm. 'Emily!' he called his wife. 'Come quickly, quickly!'

Frightened little Mrs. Dickinson came running to the other side of the chair, and took one look at the item her husband pointed out to her. 'Oh, my poor child, you need something to revive you.' The smelling-salts was always ready for such emergencies on the shelf in the back hall, and she had fetched it in a moment.

Then the Squire picked Emily up and carried her to the refuge of her own room, where they put her to bed.

'I will send for Doctor Gridley at once.' Mrs. Dickinson flurriedly wrote the note, which was dispatched on horseback immediately by the hired man, who returned shortly with the doctor's carriage following close at his heels.

'Not much to be done in cases like this,' was the verdict. 'See that she has quiet, and don't try too hard to cheer her up.'

The days that followed were full of worry for all of them. Mr. Dickinson tiptoed around the house, keeping his usually resonant voice down to a whisper. Maggie, the new maid, tried as best she could to care for the wonderful flowers in the little glass room; but 'nobody's got a green thumb like the Squire's elder darter, bless 'er poor, sick heart,' she said to old Hannah, now retired and living at home.

That good, honest soul came bustling over the day she heard of Emily's illness, ready to offer her services. 'I've nursed her before and I'll do it again,' she said.

But Emily wanted attention from no one. She was pale, so inattentive to all that went on around her, she scarcely heard those who spoke to her. Even the buds nearly at the bursting point outside her window failed to attract her interest. But time rode across her stricken body until the stunned feeling was gone one morning when she awoke, and a sharp realization of its cause came in its place. 'Ben's dead,' she repeated several times. 'First Leonard, now Ben Newton.' Within two years two of her closest friends had been snatched from her. 'God is a burglar!' she cried out angrily. She was young, and life should have been all happiness, but it seemed sad and dreary!

Emily Dickinson, with her extreme sensitiveness, could hardly bear to think of death. She loved life with such intensity that the letting go of it seemed a nightmare to her. She set such store by those who were dear to her that she couldn't stand giving them up; and she had lost two of them, so quickly in succession! When she had read the notice of Ben's departure, she felt as though she were drowning.

If she could only have spoken to Ben once more before he went! Was he peaceful, or was he terribly frightened? He must have known his time was near when he wrote. How did he meet that stranger, Death? The thought of that stealthy messenger had haunted and fascinated her since tragedy struck the first time.

She felt she had to know how Ben left or she would never have another easy moment. So she took the liberty of writing to his pastor, the Reverend Mr. Hale in Worcester.

'You may think my desire strange, sir, but the Dead was dear to me and I would like to know if he sleeps peacefully. . . . Mr. Newton became to me a gentle, yet grave Preceptor, teaching me what to read, what authors to admire, what was most grand or beautiful in nature, and that sublime lesson, a faith in things unseen, and in a life again, nobler and much more blessed.

'Of all these things he spoke — he taught me of them all, earnestly, tenderly; and when he went from us, it was as an elder brother, loved indeed very much, and mourned and remembered. During his life in Worcester he often wrote to me, and I replied to his letters. I always asked for his health, and he answered so cheerfully that, while I knew he was ill, his death indeed surprised me. . . . Please, sir, to tell me if he was willing to die, and if you think him at Home. I should love so much to know certainly that he was today in Heaven.'

In due time an answer arrived, and from what she could make out in the brief message, Emily decided that Ben must have known at least a certain serene resignation toward his going. He may even have sensed a journey into another world.

Dear Ben Newton! She determined to fulfill his dream for her, to work harder than ever before and repay him now for all he had taught her. It was as if he had taken her by the hand and led her along the path of a cliff bordering on the awesome, limitless reaches of Immortality. He had ventured too close himself, and so had been irresistibly drawn into the strange, unknown abyss.

CHAPTER NINETEEN

WHEN THE RAILROAD was finally completed, actually pronounced ready for use, they declared a holiday to launch the line. What a day for Amherst!

At least a week beforehand, the town began to fill up with dignitaries. Boltwood's Tavern was packed, and the overflow came to stay at the Mansion till the festivities were over. On the morning of the celebration, the village buzzed with activity like a swarming beehive.

Emily hurried to her room after breakfast, away from the commotion downstairs, where Father consulted with the men in the library on the program of events. 'We will try to handle the crowd as efficiently as possible,' she heard his voice boom out. He had been walking with his head high, 'from excessive satisfaction,' as Emily put it in a letter to Austin, all week long; and now he was Grand Marshal of the day, a regular Roman general with dignitaries at his heels.

By early afternoon, the crowd was on its way toward the station. Carriages 'flew like sparks in the streets,' Emily thought. All of Amherst turned out for this greatest of occasions. However, she decided not to be among them. The hurrah and shouting of crowds were empty noise in her ears; events like this were better viewed in solitude, with no one else present to take away the vastness of them. She slipped away by herself.

The day was hot and dusty; the June roses dropped their petals before the sun, and the meadow stream longed for water to soften its parched banks, caked and cracked by the heat. Emily walked slowly, trailing her sunbonnet across the grass. The unusual warmth for early summer made her dreamy, though she was excited, too, at the thought of seeing the train, *their* train, come rolling in on its trial run. Father's dream would be realized at long last.

She crossed a little footbridge over the stream, and went on toward the woods. It was Professor Tyler's wood, just bordering the Dickinson property. From the edge of it she should be able to see the train just as it rounded the bend on its way to Belchertown. She hoped the Professor would not happen to see her, nor any prying eyes of villagers seek to discover why she was here alone instead of being among the merrymakers in town.

At last she reached the spot she had decided upon, a little clearing from which the twin silver ribbons could be seen flashing in the sunlight. It wouldn't be long now till they would be covered for an instant with moving metal and power as the cars roared by. She sat down on a fallen log to wait.

She had not long. Faintly, at first in the distance she heard the engine mumbling, and then, growing louder and louder with every turn of the wheels, it suddenly became a deafening bellow, coupled with a shriek from the whistle as it came around the corner. There it was at last! What a majestic sort of monster! Tearing along, heaving smoke from its forehead, it seemed to speak of untold wonders in an age to come, of distance dwarfed by speed, of miracles wrought by power and science. There was something amusing about it, too. Like a huge animal making an enormous fuss as it streaked along. She could not help smiling as it tore past. She watched till the last trail of smoke disappeared from the valley, and then hurried home lest any of the visitors miss Squire Dickinson's elder daughter. She had had the thrill of seeing the train by herself; she was satisfied to return now to Father's guests.

Luckily, none of them had come back yet. She went straight

to her room and put on her father's favorite among all her frocks, a pale blue, flowered organdy, with velvet streamers run through it at the waist and tied in a bow at the back. She clipped a small bouquet from the sweet-pea vines, and knotting them together, fastened the cluster to the velvet in front, the perfect complement to the print in the dress. She wanted to look especially well this evening; she owed that much to Father for having run off by herself during his hour of triumph.

Mother and Vinnie came on ahead in the family cabriolet, and the Squire would be there shortly with the other executives. Vinnie's eyes sparkled as she described the celebration. 'You never saw such a mob, Emily! And such cheering! Father was a real hero, we were so proud. I think he missed you, though, Em. He could see from the platform that your place in the carriage was empty.'

'I suppose he could. I'm sorry.' There was genuine regret in Emily's voice. 'But you know how I loathe crowds, and I don't believe I could have survived in this heat if I'd gone with you.'

'Well, you certainly look cool and fresh now, Em!' Vinnie was envious. 'I'm so hot and wilted, like a piece of damp cheesecloth! And you look like a garden flower.'

Emily laughed her away, but she had the pleasure of seeing her father's eyes light up when she herself admitted him on his arrival with the group of men. 'Gentlemen, my elder daughter, Emily,' he presented her grandly.

She put herself out to be gracious to them all. At the table she was more like herself than she had been since the news of Ben's death that had shocked her into silence and indifference to the life that flowed around her. She sat next to Doctor Holland, an old friend of the family, one of whom she was especially fond.

He was employed by the *Springfield Republican* to write a column on religion for the home, and his face held that kindly geniality touched with humor which marks those who have an intuitive knowledge of men's souls. He sensed that Emily had been hurt

181

and sought to draw her out of her lethargy, at the same time showing his sympathy.

'Will you come to visit us this fall?' he asked her. 'My wife made me promise not to leave until you and Vinnie had accepted our invitation. She is anxious to see you again.'

'We must wait for Father's verdict,' Emily told him. 'You know he likes to have charge of our lives! But I would enjoy being with you and Elizabeth, I know.'

'Then I shall get your father's permission tonight! Our life is simple, as you will discover, but sometimes I think a change is the best medicine one can take.' It was the only reference he made to Emily's state of mind, and she was grateful, for she saw he understood.

It was late when the last guest departed, after the men had toasted the railroad with the Squire's best Burgundy, after the last round of speeches had been made. The long, wearing day was over at last for all of them; Mrs. Dickinson and Vinnie were ready for bed at once, but the head of the house went into the library to mull over the events of the past few days which had occurred one after another with such swiftness his head swam giddily, for all his stately bearing.

When Emily was sure her mother and Vinnie were asleep, she crept downstairs again, and opened the library door. 'May I come in?' she asked softly.

Her father, deep in his chair, looked up in surprise. 'Emily, child! What are you doing up at this hour?'

'I thought I might share the fun with you, Father. Don't deny you were going over every step of the way, struggle and all, until the great moment arrived today!'

The Squire's face came as close as it ever did to a smile. 'You're right, Emily. It was a great moment, and I did want to look over it once more. Did you notice Sweetser tonight? I thought he was going to burst his waistcoat.'

Emily laughed. 'I think he'd have been justified!'

'Yes,' her father admitted, 'I couldn't have swung the stock company without Sweetser's help. And did you see old Colonel Smith and his wife right in the front row again? But I forgot' — part of his customary graveness came back; 'why weren't you there this afternoon? When Tom drove up without you in the carriage, I was disappointed. It was your place to have come,' he reproved her mildly.

'I realize that, Father. But you know how I hate the push and surge of crowds. I'm frantic in them.'

'But I wanted so much to have you see the train, Emily. You, more than any of the others, seemed to grasp what it means to the future of the world.'

'I saw it, Father,' she said quietly.

'You did? But how? You can't get a good view from here. Were you at the back of the crowd?' he asked hopefully.

She shook her head. 'I walked over to Professor Tyler's wood — the railroad runs just behind that little clearing — and I found a seat reserved for me on a fallen log. Oh, it was a wonderful view, Father! The train passed by me not three feet away. I know the thrill I felt was greater than if I'd been amid the shouting and cheers.'

Her father said, 'Yes, I suppose so.' But his expression told her plainly that he thought this only another manifestation that he had been blessed (or cursed!) with a changeling. Charming, it was true, but a changeling indeed. 'Come. He lit a candle with his usual deliberateness and blew out the oil lamp. 'It is nearly midnight and I am worn out with glory!' Then, just as they started up, 'You conducted yourself well this evening,' he commented by way of praising her as a compensation for his shortness.

'Thank you, Father.' She went on ahead, so that he would not see her smile.

❧

IN THE DAYS that followed, she often stopped her work to watch

183

the train go by. From her bedroom window she could see it snorting along its steel road far away, and when her ears detected its sharp warning, she would put aside her work and gaze out of the pane till it went past. 'It's alive,' she thought. 'A proud but noisy creature. Let me see ——' She took up her pen, and eventually the lines came:

> I like to see it lap the miles,
> And lick the valleys up,
> And stop to feed itself at tanks;
> And then, prodigious, step
>
> Around a pile of mountains,
> And supercilious, peer
> In shanties by the sides of roads;
> And then a quarry pare
>
> To fit its sides, and crawl between,
> Complaining all the while
> In horrid, hooting stanza;
> Then chase itself down hill
>
> And neigh like Boanerges;
> Then, punctual as a star,
> Stop — docile and omnipotent —
> At its own stable door.

CHAPTER TWENTY

I N THE AUTUMN, Emily and Vinnie, having secured Father's permission, betook themselves to Springfield to visit the Hollands. It was not an extraordinary sojourn. Doctor Holland and his wife were simple people, and the life they led was a simple, peaceful one. But the change was good for Emily; she basked in the serenity of the household and enjoyed long talks on literary subjects with the Doctor. She was delighted to see Mr. Samuel Bowles, the editor of the *Republican*, also an old family friend. Spurred on by her wit, he cracked jokes with her and called her his 'rascal.' His was a lively, colorful presence, and she enjoyed it to the utmost.

But the value in their Springfield stay lay in the fact that Emily saw for the first time the open worship of a friendly, even intimate God, such as she had longed for during the bleak, dreary services at home. She had always felt close to God when left to herself; it troubled her to have to fear Him formally at prayers and in church.

'Doctor Holland speaks to God as if He were sitting here among us,' she thought, as the good man conducted morning services in his own unique way after breakfast the second day. 'Why shouldn't we always be this near to God, since in a way we are part of Him?' The idea startled her as it flashed across her mind; she would have to work on it when she got home. For the moment she knew a great peacefulness and comfort in this kindly atmosphere.

And the calmness was carried over to the days following their return to Amherst. Whenever the daily duties grew too irksome, whenever the Squire let loose a storm of criticism or grew coldly silent, whenever the string of life became tangled and knotted, she dwelt upon the hope and strength and comfort she had found in Springfield; and it calmed and soothed her riled senses.

She sent Doctor Holland a few of her poems, shyly, hesitantly, but with the feeling that he could appreciate them if they had worth, and that he would know whether others would care to read them. He was the literary editor of the *Republican*; he wrote under the name of Timothy Titmouse. His column contained kindly advice on religion, and sometimes, to illustrate his point, he would write a poem or two, simple, homely stanzas that the ordinary reader could grasp.

He was impressed, even amazed, at Emily's lines. He was a bit bewildered, though he sensed they were profound, extraordinary, too much so for the common man, he thought. They would never be understood. So he wrote to her, praising her poems, but advising her against publishing them, as he said they were 'too ethereal.'

This only strengthened Emily's determination to keep her creations to herself. There was joy enough in the writing itself; public approval wasn't important; the important thing was to find the thought, and to make it a work of beauty. She spent many hours thinking this out.

Mr. Dickinson became so deeply involved in politics that he was elected Representative to Congress and carried off to Washington. He parted from his family in anxiety. 'Do be careful,' he urged Mrs. Dickinson. 'Be sure to bolt all the doors and windows every night.'

'We'll be safe, don't worry, Edward,' his wife placated him. 'Maggie and Tom are here, too, you know.'

'Yes, but three women alone — if only Austin were home I would be able to leave with an easy mind.' He was still worried, haunted with fears for his feminine charges, but at last he went, handing out a thousand and one instructions to all three of them.

His letters, after he arrived in Washington, showed the deepest concern for his family; it was plain to see how much he missed them, missed caring for them.

During the third month of 1854, spring caught March by the coat-tails, and rode through Amherst a month early. Such amazingly warm weather had never been experienced by the oldest settlers. Doors and windows were thrown open, fires went out, uncommonly sultry breezes stirred the buds. 'The thermometer stands at seventy — imagine!' Mrs. Dickinson observed with astonishment to the girls.

Emily, who wished to make the most of such weather, was out-of-doors every moment possible. 'The ides of March, the ides of March,' she said that afternoon as she had said once before. 'Surely there must be something brewing, the elements are in such an extraordinary mood!'

Even as she spoke, the yellow stage came clattering down the road and stopped before the gate. The coachman handed her a letter addressed to all of them; recognizing Father's seal, she broke it eagerly. 'Mother, Vin!' she called out as she entered the house a moment later, 'Father wants us to come to Washington!'

Such a flurry of excitement as this news caused was not rivaled even by Commencement. The seamstress was summoned at once, to hem, to sew new things, and to repair passable ones. Emily at first was loath to leave Amherst, but Father sent another letter asking her to come, though he would not 'insist,' he said. So, for his sake, she entered into the preparations with the others.

There were fittings every day, and every day boxes arrived from Boston — shawls, bonnets, ribbons, shoes, everything they might need for the trip; they would be in Washington for some weeks.

'We shall be buried under finery by the time we arrive!' declared Emily. 'And Mrs. Emmet will expire from overwork.'

The seamstress looked up, her mouth full of pins. 'Now, don't

187

bother your head about me!' she managed to get out, hissing a little through the sharp points. 'I'm happy to ready you for such a grand trip.'

'What jewelry do you want to take, Em?' Vinnie had a little box she planned to put in the trunk. 'Your best brooch, of course, and what else?'

'Take whatever you think is necessary' — Emily left the details to her practical sister. 'I am going for a final walk.'

She called her big dog, Carlo, which Father had given her before he left, and the two of them set off. The unseasonable warmth passed and now it was chilly again, but there had been a thaw that morning, and it was possible to cross the fields. She found herself going in the direction of the little pond where she had sat and dreamed on the afternoon so long ago when her late return had caused such a tempest, to say nothing of a broken plate!

Now the shadows were lengthening over the pond once more, but Emily made no move to hurry. She would stay to see the sunset; Father was not at home, and Mother was too busy to notice her absence. Besides, Emily had kept so much to herself since their visit with the Hollands, her mother was used to this habit of wanting to be alone.

The little clearing was bare and wintry now, but the ice in the water had melted with the thaw, and as the sun went down the colors seemed to fall into the pond from the sky like scraps from some bright-colored broom. There were no flowers, no green leaves or grass to cast reflections, only the rainbow hues of a sky swept with the brilliant brush of sunset. There must be a gay housewife up there!

> She sweeps with many-colored brooms,
> And leaves the shreds behind;
> Oh, housewife in the evening west,
> Come back, and dust the pond!
>
> You dropped a purple ravelling in,
> You dropped an amber thread; . . .

More would come to her later. She lingered at the favored spot till the brooms faded softly into stars, and then she came away. 'Good-bye,' she whispered. 'I'll be back.' Carlo had gone roaming, but his long tail plumed out of the underbrush at her call, and they returned to the Mansion.

Austin came to call for his mother and sisters the next morning. He was to escort the three to Washington, for it was a long, tedious journey, four changes to be made along the route, and the Squire would not think of allowing his ladies to travel alone.

Austin was pleased at the prospect before them. 'You will be the belles of Washington!' he avowed when at last they had arrived. 'I wish I could stay to see it!'

'Why don't you?' suggested Emily. 'I cannot speak for our popularity, but think of the fun it would be to see Washington.'

'Please do, Austin,' begged Vinnie.

But he shook his head. 'Lead me not into temptation,' he quoted. 'If I'm to join Father's law firm, I must get my degree.' He was at Harvard in the law school now and went back that night.

Washington at last! Emily was delighted to find it was already spring in the capital city. The air was soft, and the golden green of maple blossoms filled the skies, in sunny places the grass was already in its summer dress. It was hard to believe that winter still held Amherst in its icy grasp.

And how different the city was from the elegantly plain New England town! The whole atmosphere was leisurely, lackadaisical, and rife with color and the heavy scents of southern growth. As they rode along the wide, muddy boulevards to Cratchett's, the boarding-house where Father had rented rooms, Emily took in the new scene with an avid eye. Men strolled, not walked, in the streets, most of them with a gorgeously dressed lady on one arm. Wide hats and parasols formed circles of gay color all along the way.

'Look at that one, Emily!' Vinnie pointed out the window with a nod of her head. 'Do you think our gowns can compete with all these?'

'What's more important, can we match wits with 'em?' demanded Emily, who had been wondering whether she would be equal to the fashionable and sophisticated society.

When, on their first levee, they entered Willard's, the hotel that served as a stopping place for officials and men of affairs from all over the country, she had a moment of panic; it took all her will power to keep from withdrawing her arm from Father's and rushing back to the boarding-house.

The sea of faces, a mass of unfamiliar ovals, swayed before her as they had done during the first days at Mount Holyoke, only these were dressed in the glitter and finery of cosmopolitan diplomatic circles instead of the simple garb of schoolgirls. It was almost terrifying. But as soon as her father presented them to a noted Senator, his wife, and two daughters, Emily found her fears dissolving. People were, after all, nothing more than human beings, wherever you went. Some were more educated, more brilliantly decked out than others, but essentially they were all the same. She had not been wrong when she had quipped to Helen Fisk so many years ago that perhaps 'the world was provincial, too.'

Since human beings were among her chief concerns, Emily responded to the diversity of personalities as a finely strung instrument vibrates at the merest touch from an outside force. She was soon asking questions and answering those of others eagerly, voicing her opinion, when it was sought, with a complete lack of self-consciousness and offering some idea voluntarily when the subject roused her. And there was so much here to stir one's brain!

As she went from group to group, meeting different individuals, it seemed to her that every vital issue in the world of men was under discussion, as well as the trivia and banter of light conversation which becomes an art among well-equipped minds. She enjoyed exercising her intellect, realizing that it was ripe for the challenge; she had been saving up for such a time as this all her life.

Father, beaming with happiness now that his family was with him, accused himself inwardly of sinful pride in his auburn-haired daughter for her brilliance, wit, and charm. He prayed Heaven to forgive him, but he couldn't help it.

Washington in 1854, beneath its indolence and gaiety, was seething with the burning question of slavery. The Kansas-Nebraska Bill had just been passed to the fury of the Whigs. Douglas and Sumner were at a white heat in debates on the subject. Emily, who read the *Springfield Republican* from cover to cover in an effort to judge the situation, found her study stood her in good stead. Now she was able to discuss slavery with any of them, with a good deal more intelligence than most of the women.

'Did you notice how those Senators talked to Emily?' Mrs. Dickinson remarked to the Squire when they retired that night. 'Just like an equal!'

'I dare say she is the equal, and more, of many of them,' he answered dryly. He was impatient with the pro-slavery attitude of the Southerners in Washington. Then he went on: 'Yes, they liked our Emily. I often think she is more unusual than we realize, my dear. She has so many different sides to her nature.'

'Yes, Edward, sometimes it frightens me, especially the faraway look that comes into her eyes. I hope this vacation will draw her completely out.' So spoke Mrs. Dickinson, who never thought to discover what might be the cause of her daughter's dreamy gaze.

Emily, meanwhile, did feel herself 'drawn out.' She opened like a flower in the sunshine of the attention she received, in the constant stimulation of new faces and new ideas.

Willard's, where celebrities from all the walks of life might be seen at any hour at the bar, in the dining-halls, or in the card-rooms, was the scene of most of the formal gatherings. As they were finishing high tea there a week after their arrival, Vinnie whispered to Emily, 'I'll wager we've met more people here today than we do in a year at home!'

'It's like a constant Commencement Day tea — only not quite

191

so bucolic — with a shift in the scenery of faces every day!' Emily laughed. 'I shall be continually drunk from exhilaration if this keeps up!'

Indeed she was flushed, her red-brown eyes had a clear, golden transparency about them, her lips parted with laughter at the least provocation. She noticed now that someone was coming toward them — a handsomely dressed woman, accompanied by an officer in a dark blue uniform, was stretching both arms to them as she hurried across the room. But it was not until she had come quite close, and Emily saw the candid blue eyes and brilliant smile, that she recognized Helen Fisk Hunt. 'Helen! Helen Fisk. How wonderful to see you!' She took both hands and held them as she looked over her old friend. Helen had most certainly become a distinguished matron of Washington society.

'Emily dear! So you finally came to the capital at last! I can hardly believe it! You should have come long ago, anyone with a brain like yours.' She chatted on. 'And here is Vinnie, and Mrs. Dickinson! What a pleasure to see you all! Oh! Forgive me, Edward!' She turned to her husband at last. 'This is my beloved Emily, of whom you've heard me speak so often, and . . .' She introduced them all. She was glittering and brilliant, as if she had lived in diplomatic circles all her life.

Her husband, on the other hand, was reserved, even grave, until his humorous smile lit up his sallow, deeply lined face. He looked older than he was, and he seemed to regard his wife somewhat as an amusing child. He was gracious and charming and, as Emily sensed after a few moments of conversation, as much a scholar in his way as she in hers. While Helen received the Amherst gossip from Mrs. Dickinson and Vinnie, her husband and Emily discovered a joint interest in Infinity.

'Come, Edward, we must fly!' Helen linked her arm in his after a few moments. 'We have cards to a supper and a ball yet tonight,' she explained. 'We must plan to see you again, however. Of course you will go to a ball while you're here, won't you?'

The girls looked at one another. 'We haven't danced since the P.O.M. meetings broke up,' murmured Vinnie in an undertone; Father was approaching.

'Oh!' Really, it was a shame, Helen thought, for anyone to stay buried in Amherst when there was a place like Washington. 'Well, at any rate, you can come and watch! The balls here are so beautiful, and the dances are of the latest — the waltz, the german, the quadrille — I'll see that you receive cards. Farewell for now!' She moved away at her husband's side, smiling and nodding to acquaintances here and there among the elaborately uniformed representatives of a dozen countries.

'Helen is a butterfly,' smiled Emily, 'but she has a warm heart.'

'What did you think of her husband?' inquired Vinnie slyly. 'I didn't have a chance to form an opinion!'

Emily pinched her sister's arm. 'He interested me enormously,' she said.

Helen remembered her promise, and the Dickinsons were soon invited to a ball which the Hunts also attended. Vinnie found partners who were willing to teach her the more intricate steps she did not know, but Emily sat with Lieutenant Hunt behind the protecting fan of potted palms and discussed 'mysteries.' He was a mathematician, she learned, basing his suppositions on mathematical formulas. For more than an hour they conversed together, until the Squire came to carry his daughter off to meet some Senator.

Lieutenant Hunt sought out his wife, surrounded by an admiring cordon of partners and claimed a dance. 'Your friend Emily is all you predicted,' he told her as they moved around the hall, 'but not in the least the lofty intellectual I expected!'

'But I mentioned that she could sparkle,' protested Helen. 'She could be a star in any society! You were lucky if she opened up and spoke to you seriously. I've never been able to do it. She always laughs me off with trifles!'

'Maybe it's because she doesn't get a chance when you're talking,' her husband suggested, laughing at her.

'You are mean, Edward Hunt!' pouted his wife. 'But I'm glad you had the chance to meet Emily Dickinson, anyway. If she would write, one sentence of hers would outlive a book of mine — you should have read her compositions at school!' Then she sighed. 'But I'm afraid Amherst will put out the flame before it has a chance to burn.'

There were other state balls, there were dinners, teas, levees — something nearly every day. Washington in 1854 sensed catastrophe about to descend and sought to avert disaster with a round of entertainment — or perhaps to spend itself in a final fling of gaiety before the drums of war began to roll.

Squire Dickinson escorted his family to the Senate Chamber; they sat in the gallery at a session of the House and had the thrill of hearing his voice challenging Jefferson Davis on the floor. Vinnie and Emily took a trip up the Potomac with a party for a tour of Mount Vernon; Helen Hunt secured cards to the White House for them. There was nothing they did not take in during these weeks in the nation's center.

Toward the end of their stay, they were invited to a brilliant state dinner at Willard's. Cabinet members, ambassadors, and Supreme Court judges were there. Emily, dressed in soft flowered muslin, her burnished hair lighting up her pale face, was a spirit bright enough to liven any gathering. She found herself seated next a pompous white-haired judge, noted for his sharp tongue. 'He is of the supremest sort,' she labeled him silently. 'I shall have to keep on my toes this time!'

But she held her own easily, and there was much laughter and conversation between them. When the dessert was brought in, a pudding ringed round by a circle of blazing brandy, Emily asked her aged partner, 'Sir, may one eat of hell-fire with impunity here?' Her eyes were full of mischief.

The old judge threw back his head and roared. 'My child,' he said, 'the Supreme Court needs the touch of youth to give it life. I claim you for the promenade!' So the two of them walked up and down in the hall of the hotel for the rest of the evening. Some of the guests left early; others came from parties elsewhere and joined the promenade. Emily was surrounded by admirers who followed her up and down the carpeted length enjoying every moment of her glowing company.

'Who is that young woman?' asked a Senator's wife. 'She ought to be in Washington permanently. We need hostesses like that.'

'Such striking hair and eyes!' commented another. 'Who did you say she was?'

'I believe her name is Dickinson,' their companion informed them. 'Emily Dickinson. Her father is here from Amherst or some place.'

'You don't say!' The Senator's wife applied her lorgnette. 'A country girl and so brilliant. How amazing!'

So the talk went. Everyone who chanced to see Emily stopped to listen, inquired who she was and whence she came.

When the old judge had bestowed upon her his most flattering and fond farewells, Emily joined her little group already waiting in their wraps to return to Cratchett's.

'I can't say as much for myself, Em,' said Vinnie. 'But Austin was right about you. You're the belle of Washington!'

'It was not too tiring for you, I hope, Emily.' Her father was solicitous about her health; he feared she might wear herself out.

'Oh, no, Father! I feel fine. It has all been such an interesting experience!' She felt grateful to him for bringing them here — and so alive with it all! Next week they were going to Philadelphia. Her heart was standing on tiptoe, ready for anything that might happen.

CHAPTER TWENTY-ONE

HOW COOL AND CLEAN-SWEPT Philadelphia seemed after
Washington! It was nearing the end of April, and the
weather had already been uncomfortably warm in the
capital. Father, in the throes of a committee investigation, had
suggested they go on alone to the Quaker city, where he would join
them when it was time to return to Amherst.

'Well!' Mrs. Dickinson leaned back wearily in the carriage.
'I'm glad we have arrived! I have never been so jolted as on that
train. Vinnie, dear, hand me the smelling-salts.'

Vinnie reached into her drawstring bag absent-mindedly and
handed her mother the bottle. She and Emily were too busy
looking out to bother about a little fatigue. The well-kept brick
pavements, the solid-looking stone residences and serene-faced
Quakers in their quaint garb formed an entirely different picture
from the one that had greeted them weeks before in Washington.

'No geese waddling in the streets here,' said Vinnie, remembering
how the vehicles on Pennsylvania Avenue had to swerve occasionally to avoid running into the wandering poultry.

'Nor do I detect the smell of the pigsty!' added Emily, sniffing
the fresh, cool air (for in Washington the pigs, too, had sometimes
roamed loose). It was raining slightly, the kind, life-giving rain of
spring. The air of perpetual carnival was gone, and in its place

was one of solidarity and sobriety, not so strict as in Amherst, but enough to make them feel more at ease here.

At last they drew up before a stately home on Chestnut Street; and before they could descend from the carriage, their old friend, the Reverend Lyman Coleman, came to meet them. His round, good-natured face beamed with pleasure and affection. 'So you have come to see us at last!' He helped dainty Mrs. Dickinson down with the utmost courtliness. 'We are honored; we were afraid you might not care to leave Washington's gay sights for Philadelphia.' He did not give the shy little woman time to answer. 'And Emily — Emily! Let me look at you.' He placed his hands on her shoulders. 'How is my favorite student?'

'Still not proficient in German!' she laughed, recalling the language lessons she had taken from him at Amherst Academy.

He shook a plump finger at her. 'I'm the one to be the judge of that!' Then, turning to Vinnie, 'And Lavinia has become a young lady, too. How are you, my dear?'

'Very well, Doctor Coleman, thank you — and anxious to see Eliza! How is she?'

'Of course you are! Oh, she's fine, fine. But come in, dear ladies, come in.'

He gave his arm to Mrs. Dickinson, who managed to say now, 'It was so good of you and Eliza to invite us, the girls have been wanting to see Eliza for so long.'

'But we are delighted, simply delighted to have you,' he declared, enthusiasm bubbling from him like a fountain. 'Ah, here is Eliza!'

His daughter met them at the door, her rotund face, like the Doctor's, glowing with the love of old friends. She embraced both girls warmly and more sedately shook hands with their mother.

'It's so good to see you all again! I have been thinking of Amherst all week long while I prepared for your visit. I have a million questions to ask you about everyone.' Her dark brown curls bobbed up and down as she talked. 'But you must be tired after your journey! Come, I will show you to your rooms.'

So, with a swish and rustle of their bell-shaped skirts, the four climbed the wide staircase chatting and laughing. Eliza showed them to large, high-ceilinged bedrooms, in each of which stood a massive, mahogany bed and bureau. The flowered counterpanes matched the large painted washbowls and pitchers.

The rooms were scrupulously neat and looked so inviting to Mrs. Dickinson that she immediately settled down for a nap before dinner. What a relief it was to climb on something that stood still again; trains always frightened her.

The girls pretended to rest in Vinnie's room, but all three had so much to tell it was no use. Eliza wanted to hear all about Helen Fisk's husband the first thing. 'We've heard so much about him. What is he like?' she asked.

'I think he's homely as a wart; his forehead has lines deep as a plowed field!' was Vinnie's verdict. 'But ask Em. She saw him more than I did.'

'You can't tell much from the outside covering, Vinnie.' Her older sister looked stern. 'After talking to Lieutenant Hunt for an hour or so, 'Liza, I would call him quite distinguished — even handsome.'

'I'm sorry, Em.' Vinnie flushed, and looked down at the silver-back brushes she was removing from the bandbox.

'It's all right, Vinnie dear — your tongue just runs away before your brain has a chance at times!'

Eliza changed the subject by inquiring about Emily Fowler and Gordon Ford and some of the others they had known at the Academy. They recalled the old school days in detail; before they knew it, the bell sounded for supper in the dining-room and they hurried with last-minute touches to the toilette that had taken all that while.

In the candle-lighted room they found an excellent cold supper awaiting them; several kinds of sliced meat, a bowl of salad, and tempting jellies and preserves; there was fresh bread, and strong coffee which the Doctor poured from a tall silver urn beside his plate.

They sat for a long time over their coffee, Doctor Coleman, in his turn, learning the news from Mrs. Dickinson concerning all the people of their generation.

When it was time to retire, their host informed them, smiling: 'Tomorrow I have a treat in store for you. We are going to the Arch Street Presbyterian Church, where I promise you we shall hear a memorable sermon — whatever the subject.'

'Really?' said Mrs. Dickinson.

'We'll be lucky if we can find a seat!' offered Eliza.

'Yes; we shall have to go very early,' her father decided. 'An hour ahead of time, anyhow.'

'Who is the pastor that is so remarkable?' Emily felt her interest piqued by such talk.

'His name is Charles Wadsworth,' the Doctor told them. 'He bars all worldly description, so I will not spoil your seeing him with the attempt. But I can tell you that you will not be bored or disappointed in his sermon. The people flock to his church every Sunday now, and when he came here four years ago, that congregation was the smallest in Philadelphia.'

'He must have something to tell them,' Emily said thoughtfully.

Doctor Coleman had predicted correctly; there was already a long cue of people waiting at the church doors when their little party came up the next morning. The minister escorted his ladies with bustling courtesy to the usher, who, with a nod of recognition, led them down the aisle well past the crowded pews to the front rows, where he installed them in full view of the altar.

The rain had stopped during the night, and now the spring sunlight slanted through the stained-glass windows, diffusing the duskiness of the church with patches of soft color. It fell, prism-like, on the backs of pews, on the lace fichu of the matron in front of Emily, on the bronze of Emily's curls, just showing beneath her bonnet. Her face was pale this morning, the paleness of a cream-white rosebud with a flush on its petals; she swung her little white ivory fan back and forth slowly, wondering how the minister would enter, as there was no door visible behind the altar.

201

At last the organ began to play; and, as though it were a signal, the congregation leaned forward as one man, a mass of faces turned into one, eager and intent. Then Emily stopped the idle waving of her fan, for she saw the Reverend Charles Wadsworth, slowly rising on a platform from the floor below.

His was a singular countenance, dark, brooding, mysterious. It bore no traces of time or age, as if it stood apart from those elements. Framed by flowing black hair nearly to his collar, his olive-skinned face was flooded by an inner light that shone out through his piercing black eyes, cavernous and unfathomable. An inspired countenance, strong and unshakable.

There were hymns, a few preliminary prayers, and then he began to speak. The playing had stopped with the hymns, but it was as if the sonorous tones of the organ began to peal out, softly at first, and then with ever-increasing volume, until the whole chancel overflowed with the music of his voice spreading out in every direction. It was no longer a voice, but a great and mighty wave which carried them along, moving with a sweep and power of words that was magnificent.

Emily had never heard such tones, had never known a stirring so deep and wonderful within her. Her soul responded like a struck chord to each and every word; this man played upon the soul as on a precious instrument. His sermon dealt with Ebenezer, the Stone of Help, and each phrase contained a source of strength and help from which one might drink to the fullest. On and on he went, until the music crashed like a mighty thunderbolt hurled forth, shaking them into belief.

'This man holds in the palm of his hand the knowledge I have been searching for — all of it,' breathed Emily to herself as the service ended and the blessing was given. She felt faint and exhausted, and yet a strange elation possessed her, as if she were fashioned of light and air, as if the clay had been cast off entirely. The others were rising to go out, but still she sat, like someone in a trance.

'Come on, Em, are you going to sit here forever?' Vinnie poked her.

She started, looked at Lavinia without seeing her. 'Forever,' she repeated dreamily. 'Yes, I suppose part of me will.'

'Oh, do come along, Emily. The way you talk!'

When Emily started to tie the ribbons on her light cape, she saw that she was clutching in each hand a piece of the white ivory fan; she must have broken it sometime during the sermon. She pushed the two halves quickly into her pocket and followed the others.

The Reverend Doctor Wadsworth did not make a practice of meeting his congregation after the service — anyone wishing to see him could do so privately in his study at certain hours on certain days — but occasionally he came up to join the few who lingered longer than the rest in the hope of shaking hands with him.

Today he did so before Doctor Coleman and his party had gone, to Emily's relief and joy. The two colleagues greeted each other warmly, and then Doctor Coleman presented his guests. 'Mrs. Edward Dickinson,' he said with his funny little bow.

'We did enjoy your sermon, Doctor Wadsworth,' she said conventionally. 'We do not often hear such a one in Amherst.'

'Thank you, Madam.' He smiled, and the smile miraculously lightened his whole being, humanizing his extraordinary face.

'And these are her daughters — Lavinia' — here there was a customary acknowledgment. 'And my special young friend and one-time student — Emily Dickinson.'

Emily stepped forward with a pounding heart and held out her hand. 'Please accept my thanks for your sermon,' she said, with characteristic directness. 'You have been a great help to me.'

Her low voice, sincere in every syllable, went on rapidly: 'But there are still many problems that trouble me. Do you think — would it be possible for me to come and speak to you?'

Out of the corner of her eye she could see her mother's little start of surprise and the others watching them, but she felt she must not lose a moment of this precious time in Philadelphia now that she was on the verge of discovering that indefinable quantity she had sought so many years.

'Of course, I shall be glad to discuss your problems.' The great man looked at her and understood that the young woman before him was an unusual personality. He sensed from the urgency of her tone that the well-springs of her emotion were deep and all-embracing, that the workings of her mind were intricate and finely wrought as the delicate mechanism of a timepiece. 'My study is open between the hours of ten and twelve on Tuesday; any who wish to see me may come then — and I shall be very happy to see you there.'

'Thank you,' she said, almost in a whisper. 'I shall come.'

There was no chance for more just then; other people were approaching the pastor, and Doctor Coleman was waiting to drive them all home for dinner.

At the table Mrs. Dickinson was busy telling their host what a 'remarkable preacher' she thought Wadsworth, what a wonderful sermon they had just heard; Eliza and Vinnie chimed in wherever possible. But Emily sat silent, staring off into space, and knew not whether she ate the roasted chicken on her plate or merely plied her fork; she was filled with the inspiring experience of the sermon and she could not bring herself down to earth.

'Emily, my dear,' the Doctor said at last, 'what did you think of it? You haven't said a word!'

She was forced to take her eyes from the distant pinnacles and look into his, squinting at her inquisitively behind his spectacles. 'I think,' she answered slowly, 'that the sermon was too great for common praise.'

Tuesday was one of those rare spring days when the whole world appears to be soft and warm, filled with the wonder of rebirth. As Emily walked down the narrow streets on her way to the Reverend Doctor Wadsworth's study, her eyes reflected the golden light of morning and every nerve quivered with anticipation.

He was alone when she entered, shyly, with a certain breathlessness. 'Come in,' he said, his dark eyes lighting up at the sight of

204

her. He pushed the papers he had been working on to one side of his desk. 'I have been waiting for you.' He had the impression of a spirit, rather than a person, settling with extreme lightness in the chair he indicated.

'It was so good of you to grant me this interview,' she murmured gratefully, calmed at once by his presence. 'Doctor Wadsworth, I scarcely know where to begin.'

Then for two hours and a half they talked together of the soul, the hereafter, the faith one must have to live. She put forth all the questions that had been troubling her, and he answered with the wisdom of his ministerial experience. He thought he had met all types of human beings possible in the world, but he had never encountered one like this before, one who strove for truth as men strive for fortune or great honor. He was astonished to find it well after midday when she rose to go at last.

'I cannot tell you how much I have enjoyed this,' he said, extending his hand. 'You must know that you have nothing to fear. You have an exceptionally brilliant mind and the strength of soul to summon Unseen Help whenever necessary. Do not trouble yourself about Immortality any longer.'

She shook her head slowly. 'No, I shall never have any more doubt. If it is true, as you say, that we create Immortality here, by our own thought and action — and I believe you are right — then I am at peace.' He had banished the haunting specter of Ben Newton's death which up to now was still before her. 'Thank you once more,' she finished with a smile that was radiance itself.

'I'm glad if I have helped you.' He realized that he was still holding her hand and released her. 'If you feel like it, please write to me. I shall always be interested.'

'Good-bye, Doctor Wadsworth.' And she was gone from his office. He tried to resume work on his sermon, but he could not get back to it. This was one interview he would never forget. He picked up the memorandum sheet his wife had prepared for him on which were listed the round of obligations for that day, and a sigh escaped him; it was difficult to return to earthly matters.

Emily, once more on the street, felt that the earth had dropped away and she was skimming along on the clouds, wings of happiness bearing her onward. Neither thought nor reason presented itself; only a great exaltation carried her through the streets to the Coleman residence.

How odd, she thought, when she came into the house, that the girl should so indifferently be laying the cloth on the table; that Eliza and Vinnie should be chatting with Mrs. Dickinson about the latest modes in bonnets; that the Doctor should come in fussing about the price of fish. Didn't they realize the world was singing, and life throbbed with eloquence?

She was apart from them all, drifting giddily in light and space.

CHAPTER TWENTY-TWO

THE MOOD persisted throughout the day, and later, when they all retired, Emily's pounding senses would not let her sleep. She kept going over the interview with Wadsworth from start to finish — what a rare privilege had been hers that morning! The discoveries she had made answered a lifetime of questioning. No, she couldn't sleep; she was too filled with wonder, too tense and wrought up.

The night was warm, and she opened one of the windows and pulled a chair close to it. She threw a wrapper about her thin shoulders and sat down. The stars were dim above the tall buildings, the streets were silent and deserted. There was no sound but the gentle sighing of vernal winds and the scream of a train whistle in the distance.

How long she sat there in the darkness she did not know, but after a while she saw what appeared to be a sea opening before her eyes, a mist of years and dreams and hopes; and beyond that another sea, and then another and still another, the last hinting at still more which might never be viewed. Then, across them all she saw his face, the strong, calm face of the minister of Arch Street coming toward her, a great light through the veiled waters. He was as far from her as the distance between oceans, and yet he was close beside her.

'Do not fear,' came the music of his voice; 'I am here with you always.'

'Yes,' she answered joyfully. 'I see you. I know you are near, but you are so far away.'

He shook his head, smiling. 'Distance is a myth,' he said, 'a word the spirit does not understand. Time and distance are only the measuring-sticks of men' — he spread wide his arms — 'and once two souls have met, they shall be together through all Eternity.'

She seemed to glimpse the limitless reaches of time, and the Unknown at the end of them all; and she clung to his hand in beautiful serenity while a thousand years or more passed by in a moment.

Then the dream was gone, the face vanished, and the window was a square of gray light. She rubbed her eyes, shivering in the dawn and cramped from having sat so long in the chair. A milk cart was rolling sleepily down the street; a dog barked, awakened by the rattle of cans.

'I must have slept,' she breathed softly to the morning air. But she never was certain whether she had slumbered, or whether a miraculous vision had unfolded before her eyes.

She knew now, however, what she was going to do. She felt sure of herself, grown up at last, all doubt gone from her mind. The Reverend Doctor Wadsworth had given her the answer to the eternal mystery of life and death — or rather the key to the answer — a Faith which she could and would apply to these problems during the rest of her life. She would carry this priceless wisdom home with her and put it with her other secret (for since Ben Newton, no one but Doctor Holland had seen her work nor had surmised her dream of becoming a writer of truth). They would be mingled into one and become the fruit of her life.

WHEN EMILY RETURNED to Amherst, she wrote to Charles Wadsworth as she might to an adviser, correct, inquiring letters; respectful, sometimes admiring, but never intimate. And he answered her with friendly letters, full of strength and comfort and advice. But she kept the precious envelopes in an ebony box, like treasures, and let them pile up, gloating as the number grew. She would spend whole nights on her work now and delight in the exhaustion of the following day. This was her hidden life, that no one would ever know.

She did the household chores that fell to her, baking bread, gardening, making calls with Vinnie and her mother, playing for her father or reading to him, outwardly the same as always, but inwardly a different person. For each day held new joy, each act she performed, each beauty in the natural world about her held fresh import now. It was enough merely to have the guidance and encouragement of an incomparable man like Wadsworth; she did not ask for more. She had never dreamed of knowing someone like him. He was a giant among pigmies, a superior being among common men. As she continued to learn through him, she wished to see fewer and fewer people, the better to comprehend his teachings. Ordinary souls seemed strange.

Ben Newton had only been able to indicate the direction in which she might travel; he had led the way, for he was as much a seeker as she. But Wadsworth knew; his beliefs were definite and strong and he was able to imbue her with his uplifted, confident outlook.

She felt complete and whole, filled with spiritual surety at last. She was happy, more than content with her portion.

> God gave a loaf to every bird
> But just a crumb to me;
>
> .   .   .   .   .   .
>
> I deem that I with but a crumb
> Am sovereign of them all.

I had been hungry all the years

.   .   .   .

'Twas this on tables I had seen,
When turning, hungry, lone,
I looked in windows for the wealth
I could not hope to own.

She was positive concerning God and heaven now.

I never saw a moor,
I never saw the sea;
Yet know I how the heather looks,
And what a wave must be.

I never spoke with God,
Nor visited in heaven;
Yet certain am I of the spot
As if the chart were given.

Moreover, her perception of the spirit and heaven gave her a greater appreciation of life and the joy of earth. As much as she had always loved nature, its wonders seemed to have increased tenfold. 'Beauty crowds me till I die,' she wrote. She drank deeply, until she was staggering!

Inebriate of air am I,
And debauchee of dew,
Reeling, through endless summer days,
From inns of moulten blue.

Expression poured from her with this new awakening. Her rhyming scheme was uneven, her verse often free — she was one of the first to employ free forms. Her vocabulary and thought were some of the most exact in poetry. Finally, death no longer frightened her. She examined death as part of life, with microscopic curiosity, trying to unravel the mystery of it. She watched the faces of those who died, and of the ones who were left to mourn them. She was discovering the effect of experience on men's souls as she had intimated she might some day and saw things in people's faces she had not been conscious of before.

All this she perceived because the man in Philadelphia had shown her how to look for it. Twice in the years that followed, Charles Wadsworth came to see her. But those moments, too, were part of the secret, for no one ever knew what occurred during those visits. She did not mention them, and her family were too considerate of her sensitive nature to pry.

But it was after the second call he made — an hour spent together in the library — that Emily withdrew entirely from the world outside. She was shaken, like a leaf in a terrible storm, but emerged strong, calm. Any activity from then on that might interfere with her work, with the wonderful discoveries her brain made in its probings every moment of every hour, was over. For the remainder of her life she wished to see no one but her family and an occasional friend. She felt walled in with many people, her brain could go no farther than theirs; only alone could the mind soar into unknown worlds and discover unknown thoughts.

She wished to make the search for truth her life work, as she had intimated to Ben before he read her poems. Now she wanted to set down her wonderful discoveries in the most precise and beautiful lines she could write. And for this she must have solitude.

Austin married Susan Gilbert in 1856, and the Squire built a home for them on the Dickinson grounds. It was christened 'the other house' by members of the family; and as the years passed, Emily consented to go only as far as 'the other house,' where she could find understanding in her brother and 'Sister Sue.' She refused any activity which might take her outside the hemlock hedge. She put up her auburn curls and wore her hair more tightly done, in bands; she wore white dresses.

She became Miss Emily.

CHAPTER TWENTY~THREE

ALL THE CHILDREN who knew her loved Miss Emily. She had a way of making everything she said or did exciting. She had a low-pitched voice, thrilling in every word. Her beautiful eyes were changing all the time, now dreamy, now dancing with fun and mischief, and again they might be kind and sympathetic, or once in a great while stern and angry.

She always wore white dresses, winter or summer, rain or shine, and they were always spotlessly clean. They made her hair look brighter and her skin whiter. They made her look as if she might float away in a minute, and that was the mystery of her. You never knew when she was going to disappear through the door, leaving you alone and wondering. It gave her a sort of magic quality.

Maybe you would be talking to her in the kitchen — that wonderful, big kitchen with its green wainscoting and wide green cupboards, where bread and puddings and cakes were baked. And fruits canned, and pickles preserved, and jams and jellies put up. There was always something going on in the kitchen, and if you could get past Miss Emily's sister, Miss Lavinia, or their strict housekeeper, Maggie, you would be given something good to eat by Miss Emily herself.

She would usually give you a cooky — a 'rich,' not a plain old caraway cooky — and she would make some funny little joke, crinkling up her eyes when she laughed. Then, quick as a flash, she would be gone, flown like a white bird up to her bedroom, where she would sit at her desk and write and write, putting just a few words at a time on small pieces of white paper. No one dared disturb Miss Emily when she started to work.

Yet she was the best playmate you could imagine and always ready to join in. She didn't really play with the children, but she was the most important part of the game. Perhaps the children would be playing pirates in the Dickinson yard. There was a little band of boys and girls who always played together. Three of them were Dickinsons — Gilbert, Mattie, and Ned (Austin's children, the old Squire called them) — two of them were the minister's children from the parsonage — 'Did' and Mac Jenkins — and the other three were the Professor's children — Will, Ally, and 'little Ned.'

They would pretend to be shipwrecked and starving on a desert island, and this island always seemed to be right under Miss Emily's bedroom window. They would be about to die of starvation, when a little tap would come on the window-pane. And then a white handkerchief appeared, waved back and forth, the signal that help was coming. They waited, excited. There was always a long moment of delicious suspense while they watched closely to see what would happen next.

A few minutes later, the sash would be opened very quietly and carefully, like a whisper, and then a basket appeared, slowly lowered by a much-knotted cord, dangling from two delicate white hands.

They were Miss Emily's hands, and the basket usually contained pieces of gingerbread, long narrow oval cakes that were crisp and brown on the outside and soft on the inside. There was never any gingerbread that could compare with it. The children would creep up to the basket, as if hostile natives were waiting to shoot arrows at them, and take out the contents, perhaps putting in a dandelion for thanks. Then the basket would return jerkily to the second floor, be taken inside, and the window closed in the same stealthy way.

No one but Miss Emily would have thought of such a thing. It was much more fun than if she had called the children in and given them something to eat, for she made the game mysterious. If there was nothing to be found in the pantry, she would send down the basket with some little note written upon a white and polished sheet of paper. The children frequently could not understand the words, but they knew these were rare and wonderful words, for they sounded like music.

Miss Emily spent many hours working in her room late at night. It was whispered about in the village that no matter when you went to bed there would still be a light burning in the 'elder darter's' room at the Mansion. Only 'Sister Sue' (the Dickinson children's mother) ever saw Miss Emily's work, and then very little of it.

And, though they came seldom, what famous callers she received! Helen Hunt Jackson, the novelist, and Thomas Wentworth Higginson, editor of *The Atlantic Monthly*. She had many learned friends she wrote to, writers and thinkers and editors; and yet she always had time to write something for the children, or play with them, or make something good to eat for them. She never treated them as if they were children and she a grown-up, but acted as if they were all the same age. Sometimes she was as young as they in the games they played, and sometimes they felt as old as she when they received her notes and letters.

She was always on their side when anything went wrong, and would stand up for them against the other grown-ups. She had a habit of calling them all 'boys.' Once, when they were all in wrong with the other elders, she sent them a little note which said,

> Dear Boys,
>
> Please never grow up, which is 'much better' —
> Please never improve — you are perfect now.
>
> Emily

After that note they all felt much better.

She had another habit of calling herself 'Emily' to the children. 'Emily will get it for you,' she'd say; or, 'Emily understands,' or,

'Emily will help you.' When Miss Emily spoke like that, they knew everything would be all right.

The children liked to stand in the kitchen and watch Miss Emily cook, making a Charlotte Russe for dessert, or some of her famous wine jelly, which was known in all the village for its fine flavor. She always used silver spoons instead of kitchen spoons, and she took great care to get the measurements just right.

'Why do you do it so carefully?' little Ned asked once when they were all at her elbow as she was mixing the batter for a cake.

'Because I don't want to get a quarter-teaspoonful of Eternity in by mistake,' replied Miss Emily gravely, but way in the back of her eyes was a twinkle.

Everyone in town knew Miss Emily through the gifts and messages she sent on all occasions. A basketful of yellow pears, or ripe peaches, or purple grapes; or sometimes a roasted chicken or a frosted cake would come to someone who had been ill or was having a birthday, and there would be a flower or little nosegay on top.

Miss Emily sometimes spent hours putting a bouquet together so that it looked like a single flower, immense and beautiful, with many colored petals. Early morning and late afternoon she was in her garden, all summer long, usually kneeling on the old red army blanket, taking care of her flowers. No other garden in Amherst was quite like hers. There was lemon verbena, and heliotrope, and hyacinths in spring, and two oleander trees blooming in green tubs which grew in her conservatory all winter. The conservatory was Miss Emily's special room, and you could feel that it was hers as soon as you came in. She had a desk there, at which she sometimes wrote; and there was a watering-can Squire Dickinson had designed, with a long thin curved spout, to reach the plants that were high up. There were flowers like cape jasmine, which had a heavy, sweet fragrance when it bloomed, and a big, potted plant called daphne odora. Here Miss Emily would put the cocoons she found on her long walks through the woods in autumn.

ON A COLD, WINDY AFTERNOON in late November, little Mac Jenkins made his way across the muddy road to the Mansion. He had a message to Mrs. Dickinson from his mother. The wind was blowing hard, and he hurried; but he was careful to close the gate of the white picket fence. If he didn't, he'd hear the deep voice of Mr. Austin Dickinson boom out, 'Boy, shut that gate!' and frightened, he'd have to scramble back and shut it. The gate was high, and he had to hang on so the wind wouldn't push it open against him, but he finally got it closed and went on to the side door of the Mansion.

Maggie let him in. 'Hurry now!' she exclaimed. 'Sure, it's a bad day out. Wipe your feet!'

Mac wiped his feet and came in. He found Mrs. Dickinson in the dining-room polishing her silver. There had been an oyster supper at the Mansion the night before, and Mrs. Dickinson never put away her best silver without carefully polishing it first. She was wearing a lavender dress and a little white shawl, and her white hair was carefully curled next to her face.

'Oh, it's Mac Jenkins. Come in, dear,' she said. 'Stand by the stove and warm yourself. What a gray day it is!'

'Mother sent me over with a note for you, Mrs. Dickinson,' said Mac, and he handed her the folded paper.

Squire Dickinson suddenly stood in the doorway, tall and important. He came from the library, a law book in his hand.

'Who is it?' he said. 'Who came in just now?'

'Only MacGregor Jenkins here, dear,' answered Mrs. Dickinson. 'He brought a note from the Parsonage.'

'Oh,' grunted Mr. Dickinson. 'Good day, boy. How are you?'

'Good day, Mr. Dickinson,' said Mac in a timid voice. He was a little afraid of the Squire, always so tall and solemn-looking. He sighed with relief when the old man turned and went back to the library.

Mrs. Dickinson read the note and then said, 'Wait here a minute, dear. I must go to my desk and write a reply.' And she left him alone in the dining-room while she penned an answer to Mrs. Jenkins.

There was no sign of Miss Emily. Mac peeked out into the hall and listened closely for the sound of her quick step or her husky voice somewhere in the big house, but it was all quiet. Maybe Miss Emily was writing letters. He wished she would come in, and he could be all alone with Miss Emily, so he could tell everybody about it.

But after a few moments Mrs. Dickinson came back with her note written, and it was time to go home.

He was about to leave by the side door, when he heard a low voice, almost in a whisper, call: 'Mac!'

It was Miss Emily!

She was excited, and her eyes were shining. 'Come quickly, if you want to see something beautiful!' she said.

She led him to the conservatory and pointed to a wonderful moth which had just come out of its cocoon. Its wings were still heavy, and it moved slowly from flower to flower, its patterned colors making a beautiful picture among the blossoms.

Miss Emily's eyes, like twin lights, followed wherever the butterfly went; and she seemed to be holding her breath, she stood so still. Mac held his breath, too. He was excited because Miss Emily was. He heard her murmur something about 'the butterfly's assumption-gown,' and 'chrysoprase apartments.' Mac didn't know what she meant, but he knew he had heard a poet speaking. Miss Emily stood there, with her head flung back and her eyes going way past the butterfly now, beyond the conservatory and the trees outside, looking far off into the distance. Her right hand was raised a little, palm upward, as though she were about to see something no one else could ever see. Mac thought he had never seen anyone look as wonderful as Miss Emily did at that moment. He left a few minutes later, but he never in his life forgot the time when he was alone with Miss Emily in the conservatory.

As for Emily — now 'Miss Emily' to the new generation — she

continued to stand in the same position long after little Mac Jenkins had left; she did not even hear him go. She lost all track of time and duty as she watched the newly emerged moth and speculated on the significance of the event.

When the words Mac had heard her utter formed themselves into a definite thought, she turned and moved swiftly through the dining-room into the hall and up the stairs to her room, where she sat down at the desk and began to write rapidly. When the lines were roughly finished, she re-read them, crossed some out, wrote, consulted her lexicon, and rewrote. She was still not satisfied. 'I'll polish it tonight,' she promised herself.

And she did, her head bent over the paper during the deepest watches of the darkness. At last the piece was done, and she took a fresh sheet, copying the completed product with extreme care in handwriting that was bold and free, but exceedingly fine with long curving strokes at the ends of words. She signed it simply, a large 'E' in one corner.

> The butterfly's assumption-gown
> In chrysoprase apartments hung,
>   This afternoon put on.
>
> How condescending to descend,
> And be of buttercups the friend
>   In a New England town!

She stretched her arms above her head, relieving her tense muscles. It must be late, perhaps two or three o'clock. If Father should have awakened and noticed the thin trickle of light under her door, he would be worried. He did not oppose her any more — she could read, think, work as she pleased. He was beyond figuring her peculiar tastes — but he was still concerned about her health and was not above protesting these late hours if he happened to catch the dim glow of her candle. She really ought to undress.

But first she stood up and went to the bureau and opened the third drawer noiselessly. It was more than half full of little square

218

packages fastened together by many small strings and stacked in neat rows across the drawer. She picked up one of the packets, untied the string, threaded it through a large-eyed needle, and sewed the fresh paper, now folded, onto the others. She counted them — five, another package done. She tied it up again, then fastened the loose ends to the package underneath. She breathed with deep contentment as she gave a final touch of her fingers to the latest unit.

There must be several hundred poems here by now! Her treasure, her storehouse of happiness. She did not want them printed; she did not care to be famous, fussed over by a million people like Helen Hunt.

> How dreary to be somebody!
> How public like a frog
> To tell your name the livelong day
> To an admiring bog!

In years to come, after she was gone, the world could view her contribution, if it cared to do so. This was her 'letter to the world,' that she had dreamed of writing back at Mount Holyoke.

She had discovered for herself the answer to the riddle of life, an answer she would enlarge upon till her days were over. She saw that it was all One — Love, God, Man, Heaven, and Earth; Unity was the underlying motive of the pattern, and all of it was there — ugliness, tragedy, and sorrow were only the errors of man; they were lost when you saw the Whole. She had not joined the church, she did not go to the Sunday services any more; yet no one was as close to God as she: He was a part of her every moment.

> Some keep the Sabbath going to church;
> I keep it staying at home,
> With a bobolink for a chorister,
> And an orchard for a dome.
>
> Some keep the Sabbath in surplice;
> I just wear my wings,

And instead of tolling the bell for church,
Our little sexton sings.

God preaches — a noted clergyman —
And the sermon is never long;
So instead of getting to heaven at last,
I'm going all along!

She had learned what Ben meant when he said religion was not professing one creed or another, but a way of living. She endowed every particle of her life with divinity. Her awareness and love, which she had learned through denial and retirement, she wished to bequeath to other men. But she couldn't bear to let them see it now. It was too intimate, too close to her soul.

Here in her writing was the joy, the bigness, the importance of life as well as she knew how to express it. In another part of the country, unknown to her, Walt Whitman was shouting the same thing in essence, but he was a speech-maker. Emily was a song-stress. She was putting her life thought in music for a later time in American history. It was not until nearly 1900 that people discovered a great poet had lived in Amherst from 1830 to 1886.

Now she stood gazing at her work. Here, all tied up in little square packages in a bureau drawer, was her offering. To the beautiful world she must some day leave behind her she wanted to give this whole new world of thought.

THE END